ALOS ALTOS JAN 1 0 '94

P9-EDS-875

This book is from the:

santa clara
county
library district

There never was a man what couldn't be throwed—or a
horse what couldn't be rode.

SANTA CLARA COUNTY FREE LIBRARY
SAN JOSE, CALIF.

COWBOYS
NORTH AND SOUTH

BY
WILL JAMES

ILLUSTRATED BY THE AUTHOR

CHARLES SCRIBNER'S SONS
NEW YORK AND LONDON
1931

SANTA CLARA COUNTY LIBRARY

3 3305 01361 9378

COPYRIGHT, 1923, 1924, BY
CHARLES SCRIBNER'S SONS

COPYRIGHT, 1923, BY
CURTIS PUBLISHING CO

Printed in the United States of America

X 917.8
J29c

SANTA CLARA COUNTY FREE LIBRARY
SAN JOSE. CALIF.

PREFACE

WHAT I've wrote in this book is without the help of the dictionary or any course in story writing. I didn't want to dilude what I had to say with a lot of imported words that I couldn't of handled. Good english is all right, but when I want to say *something* I believe in hitting straight to the point without fishing for decorated language.

Me, never being to school and having to pick up what I know in grammar from old magazines and saddle catalogs scattered in cow camps would find plenty of territory for improvement in the literary range, but as the editors and publishers seem to like my efforts the way I put 'em out, which is natural and undiluded,

140638

and being that them same editors and publishers make a successful practice of putting out work that'll suit the readers makes me feel confident enough to give my pen full swing without picking up the slack.

I was born and raised in the cow country, I am a cowboy, and what's put down in these pages *is not material that I've hunted up*, it's what I've lived, seen, and went thru before I ever had any idea that my writing and sketches would ever appear before the public.

For years I've felt the confidence that I could ride and scratch any horse I ever saw. That was a great feeling while it lasted, but too many rough ones gradually shook that confidence out of me, and come a time when I was told that after six months' rest I could maybe ride gentle stock without much danger. I'd rode for the biggest cow and horse outfits from Mexico to Canada, wherever I went I was on a horse, even in the army, and when I was put in the discard to ride only gentle horses was when I tried my hand at drawing and writing of the things I've lived as they really are, and it done me a lot of good to see that my work was accepted by the publishers, not so much for what it brought me as for the chance it gave me to show the readers that a cowboy is just as human as any human ever was and how he's been misrepresented by authors who hunted up material by going thru the country on a Pullman, afraid to mix in the dust and get the true facts.

But it's just as well they didn't, for the cowboy's life can't

SANTA CLARA COUNTY FREE LIBRARY
SAN JOSE, CALIF.

be learnt in a day or even a year, it's a life you got to be raised at to understand, and I've had it proved that in my work even tho it may be rough, all the folks of the cow countries are backing me in what I say, and I hear the same holler as I used to when riding the side-winding bucker "stay a long time cowboy."

Will James

III

CONTENTS

ILLUSTRATIONS

[xiii]

SANTA CLARA COUNTY FREE LIBRARY
SAN JOSE, CALIF.

ILLUSTRATIONS XV

ILLUSTRATIONS xvii

COWBOYS

NORTH AND SOUTH

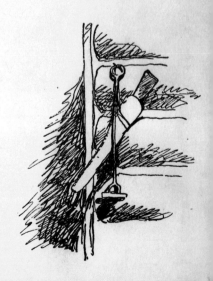

CHAPTER I

IT was early one fall when I plans to hit out for new territory. I'd rode for most of the big outfits north of the Wyoming line up into Canada through Saskatchewan and Alberta. The snow'd come earlier than usual and covered our tarps [short for tarpaulin] and saddles many a time, putting kinks in the ponies' backs to boot, and crimping the old cow horses with rheumatics.

Our ropes, latigos, and saddle blankets were stiff and froze; the wind blowed steady and mud and slush was up to our necks. And the boys from the lower country to the south was bellering at the weather and wishing they was back in the yucca country again, where the sun shined, they said, and lizards was out all winter.

I'd dug up all the clothes I had in my "war bag" and been wearing 'em trying to keep warm, but the rough weather overtook us when we wasn't looking and wasn't prepared for it; consequences is, we rode and froze all day and some more of it on night guard. I'd never been south, but all the decorations the southern hands had to furnish for them paradise valleys by the border kinda unsettled me, and I wanted to drift.

In another month the round-up wagon pulls in and the remuda turned loose; the superintendent hands us our company checks, telling us to be sure and show up again in time for the spring works.

But, I agrees with some of the boys that I wasn't going to spend my summer's wages buying winter clothes, so, when we got to the railroad six of us buys tickets for as far as Ogden in Utah where we figger to stop for a spell, have a little fun, and proceed south after we got through.

We did have a little fun all right, but after a few days there was only a five-dollar gold piece between all of us. That we used to settle down to business on, and think what we was going to do.

By noon a few of the boys had signed papers and took a job with some cow outfit what was running big in Argentina and wanted American riders for "major-domos," but the old U. S. was good enough for me, and seeing that I wouldn't be no hand at getting out on freight, I wishes the rest of the boys good luck and hits out on my own hook, looking for some way of earning enough dinero to take me to that promised land, the border country.

I'm hoofing it along on one of the main streets of town when I sees one of my breed, head and hat sticking up above the crowd; there's no time lost in getting acquainted and he tells me soon enough that he's on his way to Nevada, to run mustangs.

His brother is there waiting for him with a string of good saddle-horses, he tells me, and if I'd like to come along he'd be glad to have me for my share of the wild ones as wages. That suited me just fine, so he buys two tickets and we leave that night.

The next day when we get off the train and meets the brother, we learn he'd went and got married sudden, and sold all his horses. That leaves us out in the cold, but I still had my old saddle and I was in a stock country.

I finds all the riding I want and it ain't long before I have a string and a steady winter job. But somehow or other I didn't make a very good impression there, and I learns a lot about the reason why as I stay on (it was a couple of years later before I saw the border country).

It seems like Nevada in them days was the hiding-place for a few Montana and Wyoming horse thieves and cattle rustlers; they was good hands with the rope and bronc and shooting iron, they'd get jobs from the big cow outfits, and when a strange rider showed up on the sky-line, it was took for granted by them that hombre was a sheriff, and nary a cow-hand could be seen around camp, for they'd be most all riding down a wash, out of sight and away from it.

It was on account of them few outlaws what found the north too crowded, and hit for some parts of the California Spanish cow countries, that any man riding a double-rigged saddle with the short hard-twist rope tied hard and fast (and not at all like the native of them countries used) was suspicioned to be either a horse thief or cattle rustler, or maybe a stock detective, being his outfit showed he was from other parts.

Like one time I drifted into such a country riding a fine big fat gelding, had a 30–30 carbine under my rosadero and a six-gun in my belt. I was just taking them along, not because I'd need 'em, but just that I wanted to keep 'em.

And I rides into a ranch with my suspicious double-rigged saddle, hard-twist rope, guns, and all, and inquires if I could put up for the night. They're all nice as pie and I'm the same.

The next morning I asks the owner of the place if I could stay on for a couple of days and let my horse rest up, telling him I'd either pay or else start a couple of broncs for him for his trouble, and I buys a little grain to keep my horse in the good shape he already was.

A young feller from up Montana what'd took a little place adjoining this ranch rides in just as I'm saddling a colt what'd been brung in for me. We talks a while and he's sizing me up as we go; then proceeds to tell me how this hombre where I'm staying is spreading around to the neighbors far and wide that from my rigging and actions I'm either a horse thief or a stock detective, which neither is very pleasant to have advertised.

Where he'd got his suspicions was, that I wanted to rest my horse when, to his way of thinking, he didn't need none; besides it was how I'd asked for grain to keep my horse in good shape, and, with the carbine and six-gun all throwed along with the *Miles City* rigging, was enough proof to his judgment that I was something worth watching.

That leaves me in a fine fix, for supposing somebody did steal a bunch of stock anywheres around, why I'd be the goat sure; so when that old gadder rides in that evening I'm waiting for him and reads him the riot for fair. I tells him as to how white men must be darn scarce in this part of the country when he can't recognize one as he sees him riding down the trail (meaning me), and after I get through with him he apologizes a plenty.

But that don't do no good, for when the next day I'm riding away, I stops off the trail to let my horse graze a while (never liked to ride a hungry horse) when looking up through the pines

Some of 'em didn't like our ways in handling stock.

I sees a bunch of men on horseback, and acted like they was following a trail.

I puts two and two together and gets the right conclusion, for when I rides up on the rear of 'em on a high lope I know by

the cheap look in their faces that they'd been trailing me to see
if I'd took any stock along as I went, and they was disappointed
to see me empty-handed.

"You fellers don't know much," I says as a starter, "do you
think that if I was a horse thief you'd see me riding along here
in daytime, or stopped at that hombre's ranch? No! if I'd
been a horse thief you'd never seen me at all and I'd been a
thousand miles away from here with the stock before you'd ever
got wind of it.   Furthermore," I goes on, "if you're all so damn
worried as to what I am, look me over and, if you never before
seen a man riding a decent rig with a good horse under it, why
look again; but I'm just looking for a job and taking my time
at it, and I'm not riding for no *one horse* outfit."

But there was just a few spots with folks like that, they
meant well but we didn't get the right kind of introduction to
'em, and because a few reckless hombres from the north and
east a ways got too free with their ropes, they'd brand everybody what used the same rig they did with the same iron,
"N. G."

It seemed like it mattered more what kind of outfit you rode
than how good a hand you was; some of 'em didn't like our
ways in handling stock and they felt it pretty deep to see better
hands with the rope than they was; and that's why I guess I
didn't make no hit when I first struck that country, and rode for
the first outfit.

I guess the boss remembered one time how he was took
down a peg by a little feller from Texas (they used about the
same outfit there as we did north).   This little feller was riding

along with this big overgrown boss; they was roping horses in a pasture and the boss uncoils his sixty-foot rawhide reata, throws it the whole length with a thirty-foot loop, and when it spreads

This little feller from Texas was right handy and with his short thirty-five foot "maguay," he snares the gelding.

over the horse's neck, with all that rope to spare he ain't got time to take his dallies (turns) around the horn, so he loses his rope. Thirty dollars' worth of rawhide dragging in the dirt.

Now this little feller from Texas was right and handy with

his little loop out of a short thirty-five foot "maguay" tied to his saddle horn, he snares the gelding dragging the long reata, picks it up for the boss, hands him the end and tells him quiet and easy: "I'd tie it if I was *you*."

With them kind of goings on and with the different saddles, spurs, bridles, chaps, and ropes, besides the different ways of the folks not saying as to how stock was handled, all seemed to form a line running north and south, and dividing the cow country into two separate territories and ways of doing things; by that, a cowboy may be a top hand in one State and not be worth much acrost that line into the other, that is, not till he gets onto their way of working.

Montana, Wyoming, Colorado, Arizona, New Mexico, and Texas are, you might say, one territory in their ways of doing things. The cowboys of them States are on the move 'most always and get a lot of experience besides handling broncs and cattle. And I don't ever remember riding to one of that territory's outfit without somebody said "turn your horse loose and come in"; there was no questions asked as to who you was and nobody was worried. They felt they could take care of you, if you was *good* or *bad*.

From the Mexican border on up to the Canadian line through them States I mentioned you'll find the old pioneers scattered all the way and most of 'em are from Texas; none seemed to've strayed either side much. They took their customs and riggings with 'em and the young cowboy what growed up kept using the same.

The cattle wasn't worked in the corral, everything was done

He wants to feel that the critter he piles his rope onto is *his*
no matter what happens.

outside on the flats (I'm talking of the big cow outfits). And the reason there's better ropers in them States is because they get more practice, and nothing is done afoot what can be done on horseback.

Oregon, Idaho, California, and Nevada is what you might call the other territory, and acrost the line, they're as true cowmen there as on the east side of that line, only they work different; the cause of it is the country. The big fenced meadows where you got to open ten gates to get a few miles don't call for as many riders, so everything is worked under fence, and when the cattle is turned out on the mountain range, a corral is always hunted up to cut out or brand in. (In this, I'm leaving out the desert countries.)

The rawhide reata is about the only rope, and I seen many a good throw with 'em. I seen 'em handled in ways that was real neat and sure, and I know "dally-men" what never hardly missed getting them dallies going or coming, but never did I see a rawhide man bust his critter and tie it like the boy with the tied whale line could.

There's a lot of danger in a tied rope, and it takes many a twist from the wrist that's not at all simple to do. You got to contend with your horse and the critter at the other end, and the rope what's holding the two together might wind you up if the horse turns, goes to bucking, or gets ornery; and I've seen "wind-ups" that way what'd pretty near cut a rider in two; but the "tie-man," as the boys from Texas on up are called, being they tie their ropes, wouldn't try to take dallies as the Spanish California buckeroo does; for one thing he wants to feel that the critter he piles his rope onto is *his* no matter what happens. What's more he's been raised tying his rope and he can't as a rule get the twist of dallying, and when he gets his fingers pinched, or burned off between the rope and the horn a few times, he's going to stay a tie-man, for he'd rather risk his neck than a hand.

The same with the dally-man of California, Oregon, and Nevada. His rawhide won't stand the strain of being tied; it's got to give and slip some or it'll break. That same rawhide reata ain't even supposed to drag on the ground or be stepped on, for one of the four strands might get a flaw and when it does, it soon breaks at that spot; it's mighty hard for a man using the hard twist to get onto the rawhide. It coils up on him and he can't straighten out his loop, besides he finds it's too much rope, too far to the end.

Then again the Spanish California buckeroo (by that I mean the American cowboy what kept up the early California Spanish style in rig and work) uses a altogether different saddle than the cowboy further east; the horn is higher and wrapped heavy so the turns will grab holt. The rigging is centre fire and the cinch hangs straight down from the middle of the saddle tree. And if you was to tie with them kind of saddles you'd have to pick on a horse with a special good back, and withers or else find yourself saddle and critter going one way and your horse another.

Them saddles answer the purpose of what they're used for, but they'd be no good to a Wyoming hand, cause he'd have to work different on 'em both in roping and riding. The buckeroo

The buckeroo of them centre fire countries sets back pretty
well in his rig and keeps his stirrups ahead.

of them centre fire countries on riding a bucker or any mean horse sets back pretty well and sticks his feet ahead with stirrup leathers what are set that way. They're a good saddle to ride a mean horse, being there's some jolt it gets you away from; it rocks more and the cantle don't come up and hit you like the double ring would on a kinky back. That's why the contest riders use the centre fire 'most always in the rodeos.

The range rider of Montana, on down to Texas, rides the double cinch, but in the last years the three-quarter rig's been used a lot; in the three-quarter the cinch sets further ahead than the centre fire, which puts the saddle further back and where it belongs but not as far back as the double rig. The tie rope won't very often yank 'em off, the horn is low and small, not at all fit to take dallies on. With a hard horse they work pretty fair, but not as good as the centre. The rider of them States rides straight up from his head down to his feet, but kinda apt to lean a little forward when the horse is bucking, the riding is some looser but there's a lot of scratching done, and when the old pony quits bucking he'll most likely think there was a couple of wildcats tied by the tail and throwed over his rump.

And when it comes to thei qts, there's a big difference again; the spade bit what's used by the dally and centre fire man is a contraption what the Wyoming boys call the "stomach pump" on account of a piece of flat steel what curves a little and goes up the horse's mouth. It's supposed to keep a horse where he belongs, but I find in all the men what's using them bits there's only one out of twenty what knows how. There's a lot in handling them and a good man with the spade bit can work 'most any horse fine. The main secret of it is not to forget it's a "spade" and ought to be handled according, which is light on the rein. Any other way would make a good horse fight his head and worry, and if he starts getting peeved the spade bit is no good; he'll do what he pleases anyway.

In Arizona, to the north and south, the "grazing bit" (as the centre fire buckeroo calls it) is used. It's just a small bit with a curb in the mouth-piece and with very little silver on it; laced to the bit is a long pair of open reins what are dropped to the ground (if the horse is gentle enough) when the rider gets off.

The buckeroo "across the line" has rawhide reins, not split; to the end of the rein hangs a quirt called a "romal," the head stall is light and all neat with pure silver conchas; whereas the cowboy of Montana on down is apt to use a heavy split ear headstall, and plain.

Then comes the difference in breaking horses. The centre fire man starts his broncs with a hackamore, then maybe a snaffle bit, and back to the hackamore and spade bit both, using double reins, but just letting the colt pack the bit for a spell. When the hackamore is took off, the horse is called a bridle horse. It takes about a year to make him such.

In the tall grass countries on the plains, which is the tie-man's and double-rig country, the broncs are broke mostly with a snaffle — sometimes a loose hackamore with "feador." Soon as he's some bridle-wise the light one-piece curb bit is put on, and his work is with cattle. That's where he learns to be a cow horse and every one of them broncs gets a chance at it.

And I've never seen no better or as big average of real cow

The rider of them States rides straight up from his
head down to his feet

horses as the plains and Bad Land countries's got. They get more cow work, where in some countries what used corrals a lot they're just tied up after the cattle is put in, and just a couple of ponies are being used.

Starting west of the Utah line, 'most all riding is done from camps, and very seldom is there a change of horses in one day. There's no night guard, only maybe three or four nights a year, and that's when the cattle is took to the railroad. Sometimes one horse is rode steady for three or four days at a time; and a rule of that country, which is the Spanish California style, and cheats many a buckeroo from practice with the rope, is that the boss takes it to hand to rope all the boys' horses for 'em. The rider comes up with only a hackamore or bridle and takes his horse to saddle (I could never get used to that). The same with working a herd; only a couple of the top hands can take their rope down, but the rest of the boys sure used to make up for it when the boss was away.

In Wyoming or Montana there's no mares allowed in the remuda (saddle horse bunch) while in Nevada or Oregon they use them for leaders, they're called "bell mares" and keep the saddle horses together by just being present. The cause of the difference in them two ways of handling saddle stock is that in one territory a "nighthawk" (night wrangler) is with them herds all night, while in the other they're let loose in little bunches and the bell mare keeps 'em around. (Sometimes.)

It's queer, you'd think — all the different ways of doing things when all the folks are in the same line of business that way; and it struck me the same when I first felt the change a long time ago, but I worked and stayed on all through them countries, drifted south, east, then back north and west again, and while drifting I finds that the early settlers of the different territories are responsible. They blazed the trails and run their cattle to their best way of thinking and each country called for different ways. Neither can be improved much, only maybe with ways that are scientific, but I guess that won't work much on open range; being the cattle is too numerous to be put down by name such as "Bossy" and "Spot," or fed careful and regular like the thoroughbreds.

The stock is all worked and handled to the best advantage and every care is took to get the best out of 'em; there's got to be branding and roping, and it don't matter so much how it's done so long as it's well done.

But there's a steady contest going on in the cow countries, each in their own rig and ways trying to outdo the other, it's with no hard feelings, and each as a rule is willing to credit the other for what he does. Like, for instance, the Montana boy might ride his bucker a little looser, but he's scratching him every jump; whereas, the other from Nevada may be setting close and kinda easy, but not working his legs much. The same with roping — the California boy can handle the reata and take his dallies in fine style, but the Wyoming roper will get his critter down and tied first.

And after you've rode through all these States on both sides of that line I speak of, you'll find that you can tell by the rigging a man's using just what State and pretty near the county the stranger what's just rode in may be from.

A "main herd" in Montana, Wyoming, Arizona, and Texas, goes under the name of "parada" in California, Oregon, and Nevada. A "remuda" changes to "caviada," "slick ear" to "Orejana," "cut horse" to "part horse," "cowboy" to "buck-eroo," etc., etc., but it all goes to the same critter and the same things and the same work, only a different way and style to fit the country.

These last years since Texas started putting up windmills and fences for the stock, the cowboy from there drifted north into Wyoming and Montana, where some time later that same daggoned barb wire cut the trails and made riding scarcer.

Then it was about time for the "rannies" to pull up their ponies and figger where to go next. They remembered how they left Texas and how every State from there north was feeling the pinch of the fences. So every year a few was hitting acrost the Rockies and stringing out into the sage-brush territory.

There was a many a time when remembering the old prairie States as they *was* that they'd give both arms to see it that way again, the gray sage didn't wave like the blue joint of the creek bottoms, the little twisted grama grass looked scared comparing with the "prairie wool," and the cattle seemed to be all neck reaching for shadscale and sniffing for water.

But a few years winding around that sage and buck brush on two meals a day, riding the same horse from sun-up till sundown kind of broke 'em in and weaned 'em away from the tall grass countries. There was no guard to be stood and that helped some, and again it was pretty nice to find a solid old cow camp with a dry floor and a roof when the sleet and snow started coming.

Then came a time after them few years when, in that centre fire country, spots was located where fences wasn't to be found, and even though most of the work in branding was done in corrals and the ways of working was changed some, the boy with the tied rope got to liking it near as well as the prairie he was raised into. The big hard pan flats, the deep arroyos with sides of malapi, and the scrub juniper or spooky joshua got to look different and kinda good.

And that's why to-day in that country and riding along with the centre fire and dally man, you'll see the boy with the double or three-quarter rig packing his short whale line and riding both alongside one another.

In the breaking corral, or in bull-dogging, roping, and general range work, you'll see 'em competing against one another, them two riders of the same profession but of different countries and ways.

And you'll find that even though one is always trying to outdo or show the other up, there's no snickering done, instead there's admiration in the skill each one shows in his perticular way, for they was both raised at doing things in that one way of theirs, and if they rode for a hundred years they'd never change them, for in each their way they learned to do something what takes skill, practice, and nerve, and neither can improve.

BUCKING HORSES AND
BUCKING-HORSE RIDERS

The Montana boy might ride his bucker a little looser, but
he's scratching him every jump.

CHAPTER II

IN most countries a mean horse is got rid of or broke of his meanness by either kind or rough handling. He may be given away to some enemy or shipped and sold at auction — that ornery devil, dragging all the bad names after him, will keep on drifting and changing of scenery till he's too old to be shipped or traded any more. He's a mighty expensive animal, figgering all the buggies he kicked to pieces, the harnesses he tore up, and the stalls he broke down, not counting injury to them what tried to handle him. But there's a place for such horses.

It's anywheres west of the Laramie Plains. If you've got a real ornery, man-eating, bucking, striking, can't-be-rode animal of that kind, he's sure worth a lot, and if he's worse than that he's worth more.

Fact is, there's people out looking for them kind of ponies, and they'll give from a hundred on up for 'em. They're the hombres who's responsible for these "Frontier Day Celebrations," "Rodeos," "War-Bonnets," "Reunions," and "Round-ups," and they must have mean horses, the meaner the better. They must have horses that'll give the boys what's rode in for the events a chance to show what they can do, 'cause if the rider

"up" gets a bronc that just crowhops, it don't matter how easy
he rides, or how much he fans him, and how loud the crowd in
the grand stand cheers and hollers, the judges of who's the best

And scratch both ways from the cinch, as the judges may direct.

rider won't notice him, being he has nothing hard to stick.
That's where a good, hard, mean, bucking horse is wanted, he's
got to have enough wickedness in him for that cowboy to work
on — I've seen mighty good riders left out of the prize money
on account of the horse they drew, just because that pony wasn't

What the cowboy wants is a head-fighting, limber-back cross
between greased lightning and where it hits.

mean enough; and that old boy a-setting up there with taped spurs and fighting mad, blood in his eye and a-wishing something would blow up under his bronc so he could show the world and the judges what a wolverene he is on horse-flesh.

Nobody gets credit for riding easy in a rocking-chair. What the cowboy wants is a head-fighting, limber-back cross between greased lightning and where it hits — a horse that'll call for all the endurance, main strength, and equilibrium that cowboy's got — just so he can show his ability and scratch both ways from the cinch, as the judges may direct. There's when a mean devil of a horse is wanted; he gets a chance to show how mean he is with free rein, and the cowboy has something worth while to work at.

I've knowed some great horses in that game — there was Long Tom, Hammerhead, Old Steamboat; that last was a great old pony, eleven hundred pounds of solid steel and action and a square shooter. They say he never was rode, but I know he has been rode to a standstill. They was real riders that did it, tho'. I figgered that horse was part human the way he'd feel out his rider. He'd sometimes try him out on a few easy jumps just to see how he was setting, and when he'd loosen up for the last, it's safe enough to say, when that last would come and the dust cleared, there'd 'most always be a tall lean lanky bow-legged cowboy picking himself up and wondering how many horses he'd seen in the last few seconds. I've seen Old Steamboat throw his man with his head up and four feet on the ground, but what happened before he got in that peaceful position was enough to jar a centipede loose — and a human's only got two legs.

A horse is not trained to buck, as some folks think; out there on the open range he already knows how; sometimes the bronco-buster encourages him at it for either fun or practice for the next Rodeo, and the bronc, as a rule, is more than willing and might keep on bucking every time he's rode whether the rider wants him to or not. Close as I could figure it out, the blame for originating the bucking, striking, and biting in the Western horse goes a heap to the mountain-lion and wolf — them two terrors of the range, mixed with instinct and shook up well with wild, free blood, kinda allows for the range-horse's actions. The bucking was first interduced when that stallion "Comet" got away from the Spaniards with his few mares, years before Texas was fought for; he started a wild bunch that kept multiplying, till all of Old Mexico and the Southern States was a grazing country for his sons, grandsons, and daughters — they are the real mustang — more horses were brought in from Spain, and Comet's sons would increase the little bands by stealing mares from the pastures; some would get away, join whatever bunch they could, and in no time be as wild as the rest.

Them old ponies had a lot to deal with. The mountain-lion was always a-waiting for 'em from his perch, where he could easy spring down on his victim; he'd fall on their necks, grab holt with front claws and teeth, a foot or so from the ears, then swing his hind quarters down with all his strength and clamp his claws under the horse's jaw close to the chin, jerk the pony's head up, and, if the cougar's aim was good, he'd break the mustang's neck most as quick as he lit. Once in a while the pony would shake free, but there'd be a story plain to see as to how

If the cougar's aim was good, he'd break the mustang's neck
'most as quick as he lit.

SANTA CLARA COUNTY FREE LIBRARY
SAN JOSE, CALIF.

Mr. Lion worked. The chin was gone and there'd be gashes in the neck that'd leave scars many inches long and plenty deep.

The "lobo" wolf was another to help develop "nerves" under the mustang's hide. He worked from the ground up, and

The "lobo" wolf was another to help develop "nerves" under the mustang's hide. He worked from the ground up, and got the pony to use his front and hind feet mighty well. The teeth came in handy, too.

got the pony to use his front and hind feet mighty well. The teeth came in handy, too, so all in all after his enemies got thru edicating him, there was a new nerve took growth and spread from the tip of his ears to the tip of his tail — that nerve (if such you would call it) commanded action whenever anything to the mustang's dislike appeared or let itself be known in any way.

And when the cowpuncher's loop spreads over the mustang's head and draws up, he's fighting the same as he would with the cougar, he's a bucking, striking, kicking, and biting hunk of horse-flesh to anything that's close.

The mustang made a mighty fine cow horse and was good enough till, about forty years or so ago, the stockmen started buying blooded horses from the East and Europe to breed up bigger saddle stock. The stallions were mostly French coach and Hambletonians; some registered mares were bought, too — the cross between the hot-bloods and mustangs brought out fine big horses — but, man, how they could buck!

The mustangs kept a-getting chased and caught; they were fence-broken, some "ham-strung," and turned into big pastures where they could range winter and summer, year in year out. In each bunch you could see a thoroughbred, and the herds were showing the blood more every year — but the bucking was still there and worse than ever, the colts never saw a human from the time they were branded till they were four-year-olds, and some never saw one till they were ten. If they did it wasn't for long, a snort, a cloud of dust, and the rider was left behind a ridge, unless that perticular rider had intentions of catching some, and he sure had to be mounted for that.

As a rule, when a bunch of broncs was wanted out of the "stock" horses — there'd be a "parada" (herd of about 100 broke horses) held together by a few riders — the wild ones would be hazed (not drove) toward the "parada," the riders holding the milling herd would hide on the side of their horses and let the wild ones get in — then there'd be a grand entrée

fast and furious into the big corrals, and before the broncs knew
it they were surrounded by a good solid stockade of cottonwood
poles, ten feet high.

And when the cow-puncher's loop spreads over the mustang's head
and draws up, he's fighting the same as he would with the cougar, he's a
bucking, striking, kicking, and biting hunk of horse-flesh.

The thoroughbred stallion which was so gentle a few years
before was as wild as the herd with him, he'd never show any
symptoms of ever having seen a human or ever wanting to see
one, he'd forgot his warm box stalls and his feeds of grain, the

freedom he'd experienced was worth more to him than what man could give him. He was proud of his band, his colts were big and slick even tho' not better or tougher than the mustang already was.

And to-day when the bronco-buster packs his saddle into the breaking pen, takes his rope, and catches his bronc to break, he finds that the Comet strain is still there some — it's blended with the "blue dog" of Texas along with the Steeldust, Coach, Standard Bred, etc., and scatters all thru the Western States, the Canadian prairies, and Mexico. The imported thoroughbred can't kill that strain; fact is, they make it worse; for, even tho' the pure blood would never buck, the cross forms a kind of reaction, with the result that the foals sure keep up the reputation of the mustang that was, and then some. The freedom of the open range and big pastures the Western horse gets is all he needs, and he'll always be ready to give his rider the shaking up he's expecting.

I wouldn't give "two bits" for a bronc what didn't buck when first rode, 'cause I figgers it's their mettle showing when they do. It's the right spirit at the right time — every horse what bucks is not a outlaw, not by a long shot. I've seen and rode many a good old well-broke cow horse what had to have his buck out in the cold mornings, just to kind of warm hisself up on the subject and settle down for the work ahead.

The outlaw (as some call him) he's the horse that won't quit bucking and fights harder every time he's saddled; it's his nature, and sometimes he's made one by too rough or not rough enough handling, and spoiled either by the bronc peeler what started to break him or else turned loose on the range before

And to-day when the bronco-buster takes his rope into the breaking
pen, he finds the Comet strain is still there, some.

he's thoroughly broke, to run for months before he's caught up again. A colt can be spoiled in many ways, and reckless riders what are good riders have spoiled more horses than the poor ones have, 'cause the good rider knows he can ride his horse whatever he does or whichever way he goes, whereas the poorer rider is kinda careful and tries to teach his bronc to be a cow horse; he won't let him buck if he can help it.

There's a difference in horses' nature and very few can be handled alike. Some are kinda nervous and full of life, them kind's got to be handled careful and easy or they'd get to be mean fighters as a rule. Then there's what we call the "jughead"; he's got to be pulled around a heap, and it takes a lot of elbow grease to get him lined out for anything; and there's another that as soon as a feller gets his rope on him makes him feel that either him or the bronc ain't got far to go. He's the kind of horse with a far-away look; some folks call 'em locoed. But whether he's that or not he'll sure take a man thru some awful places and sometimes only one comes out. Such doings would make a steeplechase as exciting as a fat man's race; that horse is out to get his man and he don't care if he goes himself while doing the getting. He's out to commit suicide and make a killing at the same time. I pulled the saddle off such a horse one time after a good stiff ride; of a sudden he flew past and kicked at me with his two free legs, snapping and biting at the "jakama" (hackamore rope), heading straight for the side of the corral, when he connected with it and fell back dead, with a broken neck. I felt kinda relieved 'cause I knew it was either him or me or both of us had to go; he'd tried it before. There's a lot of them used at the round-ups and rodeos being that they mean business that way — that kind most generally can sure buck and will give a rider a chance to show his skill; but they 'most always wind up a-straddle the grand-stand's fence with a piece of broken timber thru 'em, and the rider is lucky if he comes out with just bumps.

And again there's the horse what keeps his brain a-working for some way to hang his rider's hide on the corral or anywhere it'll hang, and save his own hide doing it. He's crooked any way you take him, and will put so much energy in his bucking that when he's up in the air all twisted up, he don't figure or care about the coming down. He'll make his cowboy shake hands with Saint Peter, and won't worry whether the ground is under or on the side of him when he hits. When he falls, he falls hard, and the rider has little chance to get away. That pony seldom gets hurt, he's wise enough to look out for himself; what's on top of him is what he wants to get rid of, and he won't be on the square trying it.

Out of every hundred buckers of the arena there's only about fifteen that are square and will give a man a fair battle. Old Steamboat was that kind, he was gentle to saddle and handle, but when he felt the rider's weight and the blind was pulled off, it was second nature and fun for him to buck, and he knew as well as the boys did that he could buck.

Horses have a heap more brains than some folks would like to give 'em credit for, and if they want to be mean they know how. The same if they want to be good; the kind of interduction they get with man has a lot to do with it.

He'll make his cowboy shake hands with Saint Peter, and won't worry
whether the ground is under or on the side of him when he hits.

Most any bronc is a ticklish proposition to handle when first caught; it's not always meanness, it's fear of the human. They only try to protect themselves. Sometimes by going easy and having patience according, a man can break one to ride without bucking, but even at that, the meanest bucking horse I ever saw was gentle to break, and never made a jump till one day he got away and run with the wild bunch for a couple of years. When caught again, an Indian with the outfit rode him out of camp, with the old pony going "high, wide, and handsome." The Indian stuck, but along about noon he comes back, afoot. It was during fall round-up when that horse was caught once more; his back had been scalded by the saddle and all white hair grew where it had been. He took a dislike for saddle and men with the result that the next year he was sold to a Rodeo association for the Cowboys Reunion.

To-day there's more buckers like that in the hills waiting to be brought in, buckers as good as Old Steamboat or any of 'em ever was. They're fat and sassy and full of fight, and in them same hills and range there's riders what keeps their eyes on 'em a-figgering to bring 'em in and "buck 'em" for first money when the Rodeo is pulled off. If the association's got harder buckers, them is what they want; for as long as there's fighting broncs, there's going to be challenging riders, and in all the cowboys I've met and buckers I've handled and seen on the open ranges or arenas of U. S., Canada, and Mexico, I've still got to see the rider what couldn't be throwed and the horse what couldn't be rode.

A COWPUNCHER SPEAKS

CHAPTER III

I'M up on a knoll. The river-bottom stretches out below me, and far as I can see is a checkered country of little pastures, fields, and alfalfa patches, fences a-cutting up the land and a-stretching 'way up over the ridges. It all looks so peaceful and I wonder if it's as it looks. I wonder if that man out there working in his field, worrying about his crop or mortgage, appreciates or sees what's about him. There's so many gates, ditches, and bridges, it seems like they're down a hole and sort of trying to get out of the entanglements.

How many of 'em would like to see the country as it was; how many have rode across the river-flats when the neighbor was some fifteen miles or so away? When the only fence was a little "wrango" horse pasture and the big pole corrals? The hills were black with cattle then, more cattle than this country will ever see again; there was a lot of freedom, no mortgages, and you were glad when your neighbor rode in and sat at your table remarking "how good" *his own beef* tasted for a change.

There's old Jim Austin who's got the real-estate office up above the bank — at one time he was paying taxes on fifteen thousand head of cattle (which means he was running closer onto twenty-five thousand of the critters), had a couple thousand

horses and twenty thousand acres of land — some of it government land he'd bought for as low as two bits an acre, the rest
he got from the homesteaders who'd leave the country and trade
their "three hundred and twenty" for a ticket back home. It's
the same land I'm looking at now, but you wouldn't know it.

Jim, he'd come up trail into Montana at the "point" of Texas'
first herds; the cattle was 'most head, and horns averaging six
foot from tip to tip. He was a "top hand" and reckless as they
make 'em; had nothing but a string of broncs and good health.
He'd traded his wages for cattle, and every fall when the last of
the beef was shipped you could see Jim driving his summer's
wages home, all good young she-stock he'd bought here and there,
along with a few "slicks" he thought *might* be his.

Once in a while he'd get on a rampage and leave all his cattle
on the poker-table, but it wasn't long till there'd be another
little bunch at the home corrals bearing the Austin "iron," and
Jim would make a new promise, till finally a schoolmarm made
him keep it — and that was to never touch cards or "likker"
again. He got so he wouldn't ride bad horses any more, so interested he was in making a go of what he'd started.

His herds kept increasing and spreading over the government range; his little squatter's right was three hundred and
twenty acres and the unsurveyed land about him was same as
his. He wasn't crowded for room.

Then out of a clear sky came the smell of sheep; all was O. K.
at first, 'cause the cowmen figgered there was plenty of range
for everybody, *even sheep*. But soon enough the sheep kept
getting thicker and their range poorer, which started the crowd-

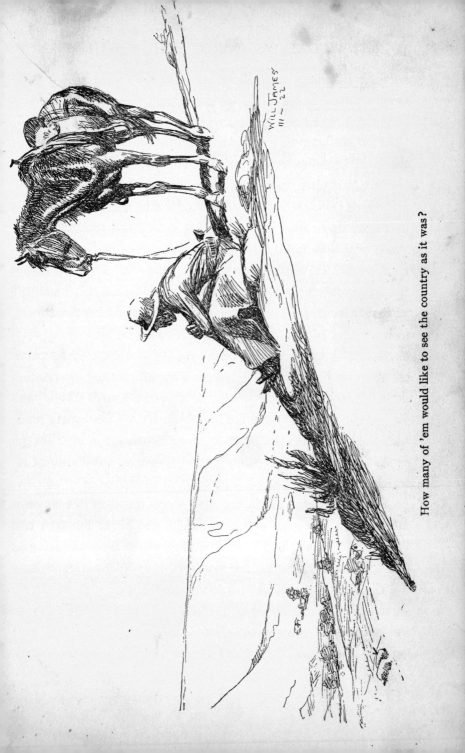

How many of 'em would like to see the country as it was?

ing on the cowman's best bits of country. There was a few
parleys without the voice of the "smoke wagon" being heard —
but sheep and sheep-herders don't have much respect for words
or rules or country; so they went at it to start spoiling it all;
and the cowmen went on to finishing what the sheepmen had
started, with the result that mostly sheepmen and sheep was
missing. The government couldn't do much; they'd had to
pinch about four States.

The cattlemen won for a spell and all was hunkydory again
outside of the damage sheep had done to the range. The dust
beds they'd made out of the good grassy "benches" was beginning to show signs of life, the air was pure as ever, and cattle
was getting fat. The cattlemen were all good folks once more
and tending to their business in the land that was theirs. They
were the first to blaze the trail to it; they made that land a big
beef-producing country, it was their home, and naturally they
wouldn't allow a stinking sheep coming along and leaving nothing of it but the bad odor.

Jim Austin rode in one day and went on to tell Mrs. Austin
what a fine neighbor had just moved in and took a "squatter's"
just five miles down the river. A few months later another
sets up a tent and starts a shack, up river this time and only
two miles away. "Well, that was all right; there's lots of room,
but I can't see how they're going to make a go of 'farming,'"
Jim said; "this country's too dry." Anyhow, they kept a-coming,
and it wasn't long till Jim couldn't follow the old trails much
more. He'd bought all the government land he could, but that
was nowheres near enough to run even one-fifth of his cattle.

His leases couldn't hold the homesteader back, only sheep. Some of his best springs were filed on and taken away from right inside his lease. Then the sheep showed up again; the homesteader wasn't worried about sheep, they couldn't do him no harm, so they were neutral, and the cattlemen went at it again alone. It was a losing fight; their range was being taken from 'em one way or another, and they hadn't much heart to saving what little was left. So they tried it in another way and speculated some. In the meantime their cattle was still eating what little feed the sheep hadn't shoved into the earth, and the cowboys was still swapping a few shots with the sheep-herder and batting him over the ear with the six-gun every chance he got.

The freighters were kept busy hauling out the nester. He'd take them, their lumber, grub, and all, and set 'em 'way out somewhere on the prairie wherever their particular homestead was at. Few of 'em had enough money to buy an outfit like team and wagon, and they went out any way, figuring on buying the next spring; besides, they'd know better what they wanted when they got there. They did all right, but not till the freighter had already left, and then they realized what a big country they were in. The first few had no close neighbors to go to and borrow from. I guess it seemed they was all alone in the whole world.

The booster had most of the folks who'd come West to homestead believing that all was fixed for them out here. All they'd have to do would be to go on and farm a little; the windmill would be a-running for 'em and the chickens waiting to be fed. Some paradise, and no wonder they flocked after they heard so much about the climate being so fine and the soil being so rich!

Jim, he'd come up trail into Montana at the "point" of Texas' first herds.

The soil *was* fine, all right, and the climate was good, but it needed water to grow what they planted. Well, they planted and waited, planted and waited in succession for years. The crop would come up fine in the spring, just fine enough for feed,

Jim couldn't follow the old trails much more.

then dry up. It was a cow country and should have been left such; but the nesters kept on hoping and working; the little money they'd brought with 'em was gone, and the little homestead was all they had. Some writers would have it that the stockman hired gunmen to drive the nesters off, but I'm here to say that I've packed many a hunk of beef on the back of my saddle for a certain nester with plenty of family and no grub. While working a herd we'd sometimes break a steer's neck or leg in roping. Jim would 'most always send one of us boys to the nester closest to tell him bring his wagon and scatter this critter among his neighbors.

One winter while riding for weak stock, and thirty miles from camp, I see one of them nester shacks in the distance and getting dark. I figgers on putting up at the place for the night, if satisfactory with the owner. I rides up and the place looks deserted; no tracks on the week-old snow and no smokes out of the pipe or light to be seen. I gets off my horse and knocks. Some one answers inside and there's a note in the voice that suggests lost hopes coming back. Opening the door I sees an old man in his bunk by the corner; had everything over him he could get — horse-blankets, sacks, and old clothes was piled high. It's a wonder he could move, but he did; that is, his head anyway, and tells me to "come in." I finds he has nothing but eight cans of corn between him and starvation. He kept warm by staying in bed or walking around when he could. He'd burnt his last fuel a month ago, even to the shelves, benches, and table he'd made; said he knew if he'd lose sight of the shack he'd get lost — and the bleak prairie outside all white without a break nowheres didn't look very promising to a newcomer — town was seventy miles away. He'd had a freighter haul his lumber and grub for him, figgering to stay on the homestead the winter and working away in the summer, and that way get title for the land. But him being a townman had no idea how much grub a human could eat in six months' time, and figgered about three months short. The little tin stove in the corner eats a lot too, and it was too late to gather "buffalo-chips," too much snow over 'em; besides, he'd need a wagon and team; so he'd et his corn cold.

The cowboy was still batting the sheep-herder over the ear with the six-gun every chance he got.

I rides back that night and gets to the ranch for breakfast, tells Jim about it, and in a short while one of the boys is headed for the nester's shack with a little grub and an extra horse to bring the old man to the ranch with.

There was many like that; some families even hit the trail for the prairies that way, with all kinds of hopes and little knowing what they had to buck up against. The pioneer stockman who'd lost his country to 'em was man enough to help 'em; he didn't have to hire no gunman. All he'd had to've done was to ignore 'em and would've got rid of many that way. He didn't, cause it wasn't in him. He liked fair play, and even though he didn't get it from some, that's the way he dealt.

Fact is, I know of plenty of times when cattlemen would find some of their cattle or horses shot down. It looked like it was done just for spite and it always struck me kind o' small for anybody to even scores that way. The sheepman wouldn't do it, it wasn't his style. And I remember, before the nesters came in, the latch-string hung out always; but with the nester or what followed him it wasn't safe to be too hospitable and leave the door open. A 30-30 carbine would disappear, or blankets, also saddles and grub; so the padlock was fastened to the cow camp and will stay there as long as there is one.

One spring, a strong warm "chinook" came, and mighty early. It took two feet of snow off the level, and kept on a-blowing hot; took most of the moisture out, and it was too early for the nesters to plant, for fear of the frost that was bound to come. The moisture that fell after that wasn't enough to wet a cigarette paper, and it blowed 'most always. The ground was dry, and where it had been ploughed it shifted fine. They didn't plant that year — they was leaving, out of the prairies back to home or anywhere else they could get, just so they got away.

Jim Austin was squatted by the corral counting the ears off the calves branded that day. "Mighty poor calf crop this spring," he thought; "cattle too scattered." He figgered he'd have to cut down the herd some more and run 'em closer to home.

A few days later Jim straddled his "top-horse" and told his wife not to expect him back for a few days. He was gone a week — and on his return he told a "wrango" to corral all the broke work-horses on the ranch, and told the ranch hands to grease up all the wagons and hitch a four-horse team to each.

The freighter would take the nester, his lumber, and grub and set 'em 'way out on the prairie.

Us cowboys kept a-branding calves but we were sure a-wondering what was up. Finally it was learned that he bought all the homesteads he could get that was *proved on*, and was helping the nesters what hadn't already gone to move their belongings and families to the railroad. They was mighty glad to sell for enough to get back home on, and that way Jim was trying to get his old range back. Though he was sorry for the nesters, he knew there was no use — this was a cow country and always will be.

The nesters' fences was tore down and built up again, but it took in bigger territory. Some places the fence was a solid ten miles long and five wide. It was a winter range, and Jim kept on paying two cents lease an acre for thousands of acres of government land and fenced that in too. Sheep had the rest of the country buffaloed and dying. Some cattlemen still run their stock out on the free range, but they weren't doing good, and the winters left many a bone pile in the coulées.

Riding up the bottom one day, Jim come across a whole outfit of tents, mules, and men in high-laced boots. They were surveyors and engineers looking over the prospects for a dam and irrigation canal. Jim got on his "high horse" right away and was fighting mad. He felt it was a new trap to beat and crowd him out of what he'd built, scraped together, and saved. He was satisfied to be left alone the way things was. The fact that the irrigation system would make his land worth ten times more didn't faze him none. He'd forgot about the colts he'd rode out to bring in and started back to the ranch feeling kind o' tired. There sure didn't seem to be no use of fighting any longer; progress wanted his freedom.

The dam was built and Jim helped build it with shares. The canal cut through the old stage roads and trails and left a scar of many colors on the side of the river breaks. Most of his government lease was taken away from him; being it was under the canal and subject to irrigation, the land was sold at high price, and this time the nesters was called "farmers" and came in to stay. There was water and plenty of it; little ditches run through the river-bottom and alfalfa began to grow. Haystacks and a few head of dairy stock were seen here and there.

Jim held on and refused to sell any of his land. The range
being overcrowded for years was mostly loco and sage-brush and
rocks. The stirrup-high "blue joint" was gone. He had to
cut down his herd and saw where what he kept would have to
be fed in winter. His own land had to be divided up with more

I've packed many a hunk of beef for the nester with plenty
of family and no grub.

fences and ditches, mowers and hay-rakes bought, and Jim tried
to get himself used to seeing it all. It sure hurt, but it had to
be. His white and brockle-faced stock crowded the fences at
first fall. There was no more rustling in 'em, and the hay he'd
cut looked better to them than the dry range. Jim didn't wonder; he knew how it was going to end — and it cut pretty deep
when his cowpunchers'd rode in with wire pliers fastened to
their saddles instead of the good old shootin'-iron at their belts.

The government didn't seem to care or realize that the cattle industry was being killed. They let sheep run in the country that could be ruined, when there was other States what might have been made sheep reserves and where their sharp hoofs could do no harm. They let the booster bring people out on the prairies that couldn't be dry-farmed. The proof is up on the benches. You'll see hundreds of deserted shacks; the land is ploughed around 'em and only weeds is where the buffalo-grass used to grow. What little is under irrigation don't no more than feed the few cattle, hogs, and sheep. Not much goes out — that is not near as much as when it was a cow country. The land is dying and it will die unless it's given a chance and the sheep are took off and put away in the burned lava country.

Some folks would call it a great country, a heap greater they think than it ever was; but it don't seem like the United States any more. Take the little town of Garrison, for instance — it used to be our shipping-point — grew overnight, you might say; new hotels was built to accommodate the pilgrims, and there'd be only one hombre out of four what you might call American. The rest was from 'most everywhere where it was crowded. Two new banks sprang up, and on the second floor of the biggest you could see the gold letters in the big windows saying

JAMES AUSTIN, REAL ESTATE

Yep, Jim had quit, turned all of his cattle he could into beef and shipped to Chicago. The mixed stock was sold at auction;

There's still a country where I can spread my loop without getting it caught in a fence-post.

his ranch was divided into small farms, which accounts for the real-estate office. It was for sale. Antonio Spagaroni had bought a hundred acres; he didn't need to hire no help. All the young Spagaronis and the Missus was working. He'd take his best pork and chickens to market and keep for himself what he couldn't get rid of. "Oh! yes, thees fine coontree."

When the armistice was signed the railroad rates went up and the cattle prices went down. The folks in the big cities were paying four prices for beef and the stockmen were losing in shipping; like one told me he'd shipped a car-load of hides and got a bill from the buyer, who said the hides didn't pay for the freight; that he'd have to send another car-load. It was a joke but there was a heap of truth in it. The cowmen were in debt and going under; they had to shift for themselves and were neglected and put back for other governmental needs. Nobody seemed to mind if beef was plumb out of sight in the butcher-shops.

Jim loaned out all he could to help his pioneer friends, at the same time glad he was out of it. There were no corrals or bellering cattle nowheres near him. He'd bought a home in Garrison, and on the walls of the big living-room you can see a few big paintings of Charley Russell's — Montana's cowboy artist. Jim knows every brush-mark on 'em. They represent happenings of the days when the range was free and open. There's no sheep or nesters' shacks to mar the scenery, and he'll tell you it's mighty good medicine for sore eyes and a tired heart.

He was studying one of them paintings as I walked in, and when he saw me he knew what was up. I'd been with Jim ever since he got enough cattle to hire an extra rider. I was his cow foreman and fought sheepmen with him and tried to help him save his little country. I saw it go under but I stayed to the end. When riding got scarce and he had to let the boys go one by one, me being the only one left, he still kept me on the pay-roll. Men for the hay-fields was hard to get, but he'd never asked me to get off my horse and ride the mowing-machine. He knew my feelings as a cowpuncher, admired and respected 'em that way. My wages never would work the way Jim's did. I was willing to let 'em go and have a little fun once in a while. I've got a home with him if I want to take it, but I feel like hit-tin' the breeze some; new scenery is real good sometimes.

There's a scope of country that stretches hundreds of miles north and south of the Santa Fe. The tourists when they go through it pull down their windows for fear of the dust. You can hear 'em say, "What an *awful* country it is; how desolate and destitute of life; a person would surely die of loneliness living in such a dreadful place," etc. Well — that's where I'm headed for, if I don't get my throat cut by barb-wire before I get there. The water-holes are forty miles apart and maybe dry when you get to 'em. You'd be surprised but there's cattle there and no fences. Fact is, the country ain't worth fencing. The only gate is on the corral by the spring. When you get out of it on your crow-hopping bronc you're free to go whichever way you please. The old trails are the same there, and I can spread my loop without getting it caught in a fence-post. It's a place where nesters never stop and sheep can't live.

Some folks call it the country God forgot, but I thinks different.

As I'm setting upon this little knoll taking a last look at the country where I'd put in so many hard rides, a little old coyote ambles up the side of the hill, sees me and stops, starts to run some more, then somehow feels that I'm harmless and stops again.   I see him limping and notice a trap kept one of his paws. He, too, has been crowded a heap, and somehow I have more admiration for him than I used to.   I'd like to let him know we're not enemies no more.

The sun is going down as I straddle my horse and head south for an all-night ride.   It's most dark before I look back. I can see the outline of the river breaks I know so well, and not so far behind I can hear the Yip! Yip! of the little old three-legged coyote — he's follerin'!

The little old three-legged coyote is follerin'.

CATTLE RUSTLERS

CHAPTER IV

RAGGED, bewhiskered, narrow-brained, cruel, and mighty dangerous to all folks, specially women, unscrupulous, with a hankering to kill and destroy all what he runs across, leaving nothing behind but the smoke and a grease spot, is the impression folks get thru the movies and other fiction of the cattle rustler and horse thief.

I don't blame them folks for shivering at the thought of ever meeting such a bad hombre, but they can rest easy, 'cause there is no such animal in the cattle rustler. Picture for yourself a man sleeping out under the stars, watching the sunrise and sunsets, where there's no skyscrapers or smoke to keep him from seeing *it all*, acting that way or being what *they* say he is.

When I speak of cattle rustlers, I don't mean them petty cheap crooks what's read dime novels and tries to get tough, steals some poor old widow's last few "dogies" cause they ain't got guts enough to get theirs from the big outfits what keeps riders the year 'round — them kind don't last long enough to be mentioned anyhow — and I always figgered the rope what kept 'em from touching the earth was worth a heap more than what it was holding.

To my way of thinking anybody with a lot of nerve is never real bad all the way, whether he be a cattle thief, or cattle rustler — the excitement he gets out of it is what he likes most, and you can bet your boots that even tho' he may be dealing from the bottom of the deck, he's taking his from them what won't suffer from the loss, or maybe even miss it; you're plumb safe when that kind rides up to your camp to leave your silver mounted spurs and bits scattered around as usual, and most likely if he sees you're in need of a fresh horse he'll be real liberal in offering you the pick of his string — only danger is, if you're caught riding one of them ponies, it may be kind of hard to explain just how you come in possession of said animal.

There's cases where some cowboy what's kind of reckless and sorta free with his rope might get a heap worse reputation than what he deserves; and he gradually gets the blame for any stock disappearing within a couple of hundred miles from his stomping ground. Naturally that gets pretty deep under his hide, with the result that he figgers he might just as well live up to his reputation, 'cause if he gets caught "going south" with five hundred head he won't get hung any higher than he would for running off with just some old "ring boned" saddle horse. Consequences is when the stock associations and others start to keep him on the move, he's using his *long rope* for fair, and when he's moving there's a few carloads of prime stock making tracks ahead of him. In Wyoming a few of the feud men tried to even scores that way; the hill billy was on horseback and toting a hair-trigger carbine.

I don't want to give the impression that the cattlemen started

The hill billy was on horseback and toting a hair-trigger carbine.

in the cow business by rustling, not by a long shot — they're plum against it in all ways, and most of 'em would let their herd dwindle down to none rather than brand anything lessen they're shure it's their own. But there is some what naturally hates to see anything go unbranded wether it's theirs or not, and being the critter don't look just right to 'em without said iron, they're most apt to plant one on and sometimes the brand don't always fit.

Like for instance, there was Bob Ryan riding mean horses all day and a lot of the night in all kinds of weather for somebody else at thirty a month and bacon. It wasn't any too interesting to him; he kinda hankered for a little range and a few head of stock of his own, and come to figgering that some outfits he'd rode for had no objections to their riders picking up a "slick" whenever it was safe. There was no reason much why them slicks couldn't just as well bear his own "iron," and that certain "ranny," being overambitious that way and sorta carefree, buys a few head of cows, calves, and yearlings, wherever he can get 'em and takes a "squatter" in the foothills, his weaning corrals being well hid higher up in some heavy timbered box canyon, and proceeds to drag a loop that makes him ashamed, at first.

There's the start of your cattle rustler — it's up to how wise he is, or how lucky, wether he keeps it up till he's really one or not. If he can get by till his herd is the size he wants it without getting caught, most likely he'll stop there and no one will know the difference, but if some inquisitive rider gets wind of his doings, and that wind scatters till it begins to look like a tornado,

why it's liable to leave him in bad humor and make him some-
what more reckless.

A few months after Bob started on his own, a couple of riders
out on circle was bringing in a bunch to the "cutting grounds,"
and in the "drags" noticed four cows with big bags bellering
their heads off — and no calves. In another drive there's two
more. Next morning, the range boss takes two riders with
him, leaving the straw boss take the others out on first "circle"
— the six cows with the full bags was turned loose the night before and the boss finds 'em by a little corral in the brush still
bellering (a cow and calf, if separated and losing track of one
another, always return to where they'd last been together and
wait for days till the one missing returns). There'd been a lot of
cattle there and 'most impossible to track any special critter, so
he goes up on a ridge toward the high mountains and "cuts" for
tracks. A few miles to the north he runs across what he's looking for, and by the signs to be seen they sure must of been travelling and a horse track was there on top of the rest, looked a
few days old.

Up a canyon it leads a ten or twelve miles, and they pass by
Bob's camp, not seeing it. It was well hid and what's more,
tracks is what the boss and the two riders was keeping their eyes
on most — up a little further there's a corral and if it wasn't for
them tracks it'd never be found. There'd been cattle there the
night before, it was plain to see. They kept quiet and listened,
off into the timber higher up a calf was heard and single file they
climbed toward where it sounded to be from, when figgering they
was close enough, they scattered and went three ways and on

The end of a wrong start.

past around where the cattle was feeding till they got up above 'em, then joined one another; and getting off their horses they climbed a high point, squatted, took their hats off, and looking thru the cracks of a red rock, they could see a few of the cattle below 'em. Bob had 'em on feed and under cover during the day and in the corral at night till the brands healed. Nothing of *him* could be seen anywheres, but he was there keeping his eye on what he could see of the back-trail and at the same time standing "day herd" on the cattle.

Bob knew 'most any one would ride right up into the cattle, if in case they was looking for him figgerin' he'd be there, but he would of fooled 'em by just dropping off his perch into the other canyon and making distance — by the time they'd got thru looking for him he'd been in the next county. The boss reckoned on all that, being quite a hand on them sorta tricks himself at one time; so calculates the best thing to do is keep out of sight, circle around back to the corral, hide and wait till Bob brought the cattle down and put up the poles at the gate. Along about sundown, the cattle is coming and Bob is with 'em, drives 'em into the corral, and he's putting up the last pole when from three different places at close distance he hears the command "Put up your hands," "'Way up there!" Bob reaches for the sky, knowing better than try to do different.

The next morning to the boss's surprise, there's no weaners in that corral; all grown stock mostly cows, and calves too young to be branded, but them cows had fresh irons and earmarks on 'em just beginning to heal. What was the original iron on them critters nobody could make out, it was blotched so bad and the ears cut so short that there was nothing to be seen but the *new iron*, that being sure visible and stretching from shoulder to hip-bone.

It was plain to see what Bob had been doing, but he had cattle of his own bearing the same iron, and he could prove it was of the first branding, and them weaners disappearing was a puzzle. The boss had a strong hunch he had 'em hid somewheres, but where? And how could he prove Bob did it?

Bob not being caught red-handed just lands into court and with his lawyer wins the fight; the judge and jury pronounces him "Not Guilty," and the lawyer takes the cattle for the fee. (It's 'most impossible to convict any one of cattle rustling, and that's why "necktie-parties" was so popular.) When the sun shines on his freedom again, the first thing that stares him in the eye is cattle once more, cattle everywhere on the hillsides and brakes — he knows it's his move, so calculates to make the most of it while moving. His idea is to clear enough to get him started in some new country, where he ain't branded so well.

He knows he'll get the blame for all that disappears in that territory, so he goes to work and takes pains to let everybody know in the town and country that he's hitting the breeze. He wants to let 'em understand that there'll be a whole State, maybe two, between him and those what suspicions. He sticks around for a week or more, straightening out his affairs, and the while telling the folks about him what a paradise this new country is where he's going to, that he wouldn't come back again on a bet.

The stage-driver takes him and his "thirty years' gathering" to the railroad-station and comes back telling the storekeeper and livery-stable man that he's went for sure. He'd seen him buy a ticket for some town a thousand miles away, and everybody kinda draws a long breath saying something like "good riddance of bad rubbish."

The stage-driver takes him and his "thirty years' gathering" to the railroad-station.

Sure enough, Bob had went alright, and arrives at this new country unknown and walking kinda straight. The sheriff ain't ever heard of him and he inquires 'round at the stable where the headquarters for the Blue River Land and Cattle Company might be found. The superintendent, upon his asking for a job, informs him that he's full-handed excepting that he could use a good man "snapping broncs."

A few days later you could see Bob inside the breaking corral of the home ranch; four broncs are tied up and getting "eddicated" and another's saddled ready to be "topped off." He's standing there rolling a smoke, his mind not at all on the hobbled glass-eyed horse standing alongside him with legs wide apart and tipping the saddle near straight up with the hump that makes the boys ride. His eyes are on over and past the other broncs tied to the corral, and sees only away across the valley some fifteen miles. Timber out there draws his attention, and Bob wonders what the range is like at the perticular spot.

It's quite a ride for a green bronc, but not many days later you could see him winding up, following the cow trails to that timber and waterhole. He passes two "alkali licks" and rides on thru the aspens to the mesa — white sage, grama, and mountain bunch-grass everywhere, shad-scale on the flat and wild peas in the gullies higher up. There's a line of troughs at the waterhole and a few head of the Blue River cattle are watering there.

That night at the bunk house with the boys, Bob hazes the talk to drifting on about the springs and holdings of the company and by just listening, asking no questions, he finds that the little range he'd rode into that day was held by the outfit. He had a hunch they was holding it with no rights, and every one in the country had took it for granted it was theirs, never bothering about finding out.

A few months later the broncs are all "snapped out," a paycheck in Bob's chap pocket, and then pretty soon a log house is up and the smoke coming out of the fireplace thru the timber where the line of troughs and alkali licks was located. There

He's rolling a smoke, his mind not at all on the hobbled glass-eyed
horse standing alongside him.

was a howl from the company about somebody "jumping" one of their springs, but that don't do no good; saying they owned that range and proving it was two different things; and Bob stayed on, taking in horses to break at ten dollars a head and making a big bluff as to how much he's putting away, every so often.

One day Bob disappears and is gone for 'most six weeks; his place being out of the way of any riders nobody knows he'd went or returned, and if you'd asked him where he was keeping himself he'd said, "home." Anyway, in a few days after his return, he buys a hundred head of mixed stock, and some kinda wondered where he'd got the money to buy stock with, figgering even if he did make a good stake at breaking horses, it wouldn't buy one-fourth the cattle he'd paid cash for. He disappears once more without any one knowing of it and buys another little bunch of "dogies." Bob was getting bolder every time and the big outfits a thousand miles to the north and east was putting out a big reward for a cattle thief they didn't have the description of. They'd plumb forgot about Bob, knowing him to be south somewhere and doing well, as they'd hear tell from the riders travelling thru.

He got so he could change a brand on a critter, and with a broken blade and a little acid of his own preparation make that brand to suit his taste, and in fifteen minutes appear like it'd been there since the critter was born. You could feel the scaly ridge in the hide where the iron was supposed to've been and even a little white hair here and there; it would sure stand inspection from either the eye or the hand.

Bob knowing every hill, coulée, flat, creek, and river of that country, was a great help to him. He'd rode every foot of it for a hundred miles around. It was where he'd stood trial and lost his first herd. He knew the folks there had forgot him and that's what he wanted. It left him a clear trail out of suspicion; the train would take and leave him at some neighboring town at

He'd camp on the critters' tails till they'd use all the energy
they had to get out of the way.

night getting a couple of ponies and hitting out on "jerky," a little flour, and salt before sun-up, he'd skirt the foothills and never would a rider get sight of him. Laying low by day and riding by night he'd locate the herds with the best beef and camp within a few miles of 'em so if they drifted he'd know their whereabouts and, soon as the weather permit, fog on behind 'em.

At the first sign of a strong wind, when tracks a few hours old are sifted over with fine sand, or before a first snow, you could see Bob getting his "piggin' string," unlimbering his ropes and testing his acid; his copper "running iron" was always with him too, hid between his saddle skirting and the lining; his 30-30 well cleaned and oiled and the old smoke wagon under his shirt and resting on his chap belt, he'd hit out on the best horse the country had for the herd he'd been watching, and go to cutting out a couple of carloads of the primest stuff he could get. Of course, by the time he'd get 'em to the shipping point, or market, they'd only be "feeders," but that brought a fair price.

The first night he'd camp on the critters' tails till they'd use all the energy they had to get out of the way. (In some cases it's been known of some cattle rustlers covering over forty miles single-handed with fifty some odd head in one night.) Bob had figgered a long time ahead the best way to take his cattle out, the hiding places for the day, and water to go with it, keeping shy of fences and ranches. At first sign of the rising sun his cattle was watered and taken up in some timbered canyon, the brands was worked over and a few hours later the herd was bedded down or feeding. The next night would be easier on both man and stock, and by the third, Bob felt pretty secure, but never would you find him with the cattle during the day. The cattle being too tired to stray away was left soon as watered and taken on feed. When they'd be hid, Bob would "back-trail" a mile or so, where he could watch his cattle and see any riders what might be following him. In case there was, he had plenty of time before they got to his cattle and had 'em identified to make a getaway; for even tho' an "iron" may be worked over into another, the rustler ain't going to take a chance. There may be a "marker" in that bunch that only the owner, or the riders familiar with the cattle, would recognize; and that's enough to entitle the rustler to the stout limb and a piece of rope if he's caught.

When once out of the stolen cattle's territory and a hundred miles or so farther the cattle are loaded into the cars. (It's done at night if there is no inspection in that particular State.) Bob's going to stick to the finish 'cause he figgers his iron is going to stand the inspection of the stockyards inspector — he can show you where that brand is recorded and that they're his cattle unless you have reason to be real out of the ordinary inquisitive and want to know too much — but even then Bob has cattle bearing the same "iron" on his range to the south, and it may be mighty hard to prove they're not his. Furthermore, nobody knows or can prove he's been out of the country or whether he's shipped some of his own cattle or not — and no one had seen him around where the cattle was stolen.

It was getting real interesting, and he did not realize that he was taking a liking to stealing cattle and making clean getaways. The herd at his home camp was getting to be just a bluff, bearing half a dozen different recorded irons and earmarks. He was beginning to use them to fall back on in case investigation was made and traced back to his "hangout." He'd made three trips to Chicago and was just thinking of settling down to steal no more. He knew this good luck wouldn't last, and besides, picking up a few "orejanas" now and again around his own little range to the south might prove just as interesting; but the fever had him, with the result that he found out no matter how close you figger there's always something you'll overlook what'll give you away.

A man with a critter down, his horse standing rope's length away, is a good thing to keep away from — unless you want to get your Stetson perforated.

He started north for another raid, and thought he'd take his own saddle horses along this time, being that good horses are hard to pick up everywhere that way. There was one horse especially he hated to leave behind. It was a big blood bay, bald-faced and stocking-legged, and when he got to his destination to the north, and the stock car was being switched at the yards, one of the old timers recognized the horse and kept mum till Bob came to the stock car and led him out with his other horse. Ten minutes later Bob was feeding up at the "open-all-night" Chink restaurant and watching the front door. The sheriff comes thru the kitchen and when Bob turned around to his "ham and eggs" there was the muzzle of a "45" staring him in the eye.

He lost his second herd to the same lawyer and faced the same judge of two years before. He'd only stole one horse where he'd got away with over two hundred head of cattle in that country, but that one horse put the kibosh on him. There was no proof that he'd stole any cattle, but they suspicioned mighty strong; and they couldn't of handed him any more if they could of proved it. So figgering on killing two birds with one stone, the judge, not weeping any, throws the book at him, which means he gives Bob the limit.

If Bob would of had better luck the first time he tried to settle down in the country where he'd made such a bad "reputation" for himself, most likely by now he'd been just a prosperous cowman and kept his "long ropes" to home. I don't figger Bob was bad, just a little too anxious to have something, and later on getting too much satisfaction in outwitting others.

Any stranger was welcome to Bob's camp to feed and rest up; a fresh horse, or anything else he had, was offered to them what needed it, and it wouldn't matter if your pack horse was loaded with gold nuggets they was just as safe in his bunk house, or maybe safer, than in the safety vault. His specialty was cattle and he got to love to use his skill in changing irons.

He was just like a big average of the Western outlaw and cattle rustler; his squareness in some things made up for his crookedness in others. There was no petty work done: saddle, spurs, and chaps was safe hanging over the corral, but there was one thing you had to keep away from in the rustler's doings; if you saw at a distance a smoke going up, one man with a critter down and a horse standing rope's length away, it's always a good idea to ride 'way around and keep out of sight, unless you want your Stetson perforated. If you was interested and had company, why that's another story.

I used to know a big cowman, who'd been fairly free with the running iron at one time and had done a heap of rustling. Many a head he'd lost in the same way afterward. Those he caught was dealt mighty hard with, and he'd expected the same if he'd ever made that fatal mistake, but he was lucky enough not to.

One day a "nester," what had drifted in from the other side of the plains and settled on one of his creek bottoms, finds himself and family run out of bacon or any sort of meat. He ups and shoots a fine yearling, takes the hindquarters, and leaves the rest in the hide for the coyotes, or to spoil. One of the riders runs onto the carcass, and lucky there was no proof of who done it, for that kind of doings sure gets a "rise" from a cowhand. A

A little "wild cat" loop settles neat and around that waster's neck, he's jerked off his seat and drug to the nearest cottonwood.

little over a month later, another yearling is butchered the same way, but the hide is gone and that's what makes it interesting.

It was found under the nester's little haystack. There's nobody home just then. The cowman finding this evidence had changed many an iron and earmark in his early start (as I've mentioned before) but never had he played hog and left any perfectly good beef to spoil on the range, and he figgers to teach that country spoiling hombre a few lessons in range etiquette. About sundown, he catches up with him and family just when the wagon and team reaches the musselshell bottoms where there's fine big cottonwoods. A carbine stares the nester in the face, and at the same time the cowman produces a piece of the hide bearing his iron and asks him to account for it. The man on the wagon is too scared to speak or move, so is the rest back of the seat.

The cowman uncoils his rope, plays with it a while, and pretty soon a little "wild cat" loop settles neat and around that waster's neck, he's drug off his seat and close to one of them natural gallows, the rope is throwed over a limb, picked up again on the other side, and taking his "dallies" to the saddle horn, the cowman goes on till that farmer's big feet are just about a yard off the ground, a squawk is heard from the wagon and the whole family runs up to plead for the guilty party. They plead on for quite a spell but the cowman acts determined and hard of hearing. When it's gone far enough and that nester gets blue 'round the gills, the rope slacks up and he sprawls down to earth; the cowman is right atop of him and tells him he's got his family to thank for to see the sun come up again, "and if I ever catch you leaving meat of my stock to spoil on the range again I'll get you up so far you'll never come down, family or no family"; and he winds up with *"you can kill all of my beef you need,* but just what you need and no more, do you hear? And I want you to produce the hides of them beeves too, every one of 'em."

With that he rides off, and the nester's family is still trying to figger out what kind of folks are these "cow persons," anyway.

WINTER MONTHS IN A
COW CAMP

CHAPTER V

IT took me a long time to figger out anywheres near of what I'd done with my summer's wages. I know I'd bought me a few winter clothes and paid out for a couple of weeks of livery stable board for my horse; then the hotel bill besides some real fancy meals had took a lot of my money. I'd bought the rounds when my turn came and stepped out with the boys, and even though I was breathing sober steady ever since I hit town, I couldn't for the life of me make out how that money went so fast. I'd saved it careful too that summer before, even rode my old saddle and made it do till the shipping was done so I could manage to live a life of ease for the few winter months.

Riding them winter months didn't strike me as anything cheerful no more, and I thought that this once I'd be able to hole in comfortable for that snowy cold period; but my pockets sprung a leak, and being that I couldn't get no comfort of what was past and spent, I begins to look into the future and wonders what cow outfit would hire a cowboy this time of year. I'm running the irons of the outfits I know of through my mind and looking into the future real deep, when I raises up straight in my bed and looks out of the hotel window to see snow coming down and adding up on the fourteen inches already on the level. Yep! I figgers the range will be needing riders.

I finds myself whistling some as I clean up, and somehow and another when I comes down the steps into the hotel lobby it don't look like much to me. There's a few tinhorn gamblers with the "hop head" complexion sticking around, and a couple of fat slick-looking gents a-swapping jokes by the big stove. I steps up to the bar, gets me a eye opener on my looks and sashays out in the dining room, where I figgers on throwing a bait to hold me till I reaches my next stopping place.

My ham and eggs is down to half when old Tom Meyers, superintendent of the "hip-O," steps up and asks how I'm setting. "Pretty fair," I says and don't tell him none of my plans, thinking that he's full handed anyway. I don't show where I'm at all interested when he says he's needing of a man at "Stone Pile" camp. "It's mean weather out right now," I says, "and I'm afraid I'm getting kinda soft, but how much are you paying?"

With a month's wages handed to me in advance I pays my bills at the hotel, bar, and stable (they hadn't been running long) and it feels kinda good to be riding out again even if the snow was deep and more of it was coming. My horse was a sniffing of it and lining out full of life. After the long spell in the stall he was glad to be out and going somewhere, and somehow I wasn't a bit sorry either.

A couple of days and along what I figgered to be about sundown (it was still snowing and the wind was coming up) I reaches the camp where I'm to get my winter horses and ride from. There's three or four rolls of bedding belonging to boys what'd *stayed to town* for the winter (same as I'd figgered on doing) and I uses one of 'em till I can get my own roll.

Stone Pile Camp.

There's two ranch hands at the camp shovelling hay to near a thousand head of "hospital cattle" (weak stock), besides a cook and a rider not counting me, and the next morning when I sniffs and smells the bacon from my bunk I know that I've settled down to some tall hard work.

It's still dark when I saddles my horse and lines out. I'd rode that country many times before and knowed how and where the cattle was running. The dry stock was in good condition, outside the few old stuff and cows with calves and "leppies" (orphant calves) what are to be brought in and fed.

Along about noon I have a few bunches spotted what had weak ones in and starts back for camp, cutting 'em out as I go and driving 'em along making about a mile an hour. Them being weak and the snow being deep it ain't long till they begin to get tired, and me knowing that the less I rush 'em the better time I'll make, I'm driving 'em easy and keeps 'em just barely moving. As the driving is kept up and the cattle want to rest they begin to spread like a fan, heading all directions, and I have a hard time keeping 'em together; but taking it real easy manages to get 'em a half a mile closer to camp, when a couple of dogies on the outside begin to get on the "prod" (fight), which means it's time for me to quit.

I had twelve head in that bunch and it took me six hours to drive 'em about five miles. It was way after dark when I dropped 'em and hit for camp, and I still had a good ten miles to go.

It takes me three days to bring 'em in, and the end of the third and late again finds me pushing a mighty weak, tired bunch of dogies through the gates of the feed yard at the camp and headed for the big shelter sheds. Half of 'em was wanting to fight but when they see the hay what was spread and waiting for 'em they kind of forgot I was around and went to eating.

For a spell that kind of work kept on. There was days when we'd be drifting with the herds and the blizzard a-howling full force, when you could hardly see your hand in front of you and the only way you knowed the direction you was headed was by the wind. If that wind switched to another direction without you knowing of it (you wasn't apt to know in the blinding storm) you was running good chances of getting lost unless you run acrost some landmark what told of your whereabouts.

The snow drifted and piled high but in drifting it cleared some ridges, and there's where the strong cattle along with the range horses was finding their feed.

Then the weather cleared and stayed a steady cold. Me and the other cowboy had covered the whole country and hazed in all what needed feed; riding was getting easy.

And one day when we hear of a dance what was going to be pulled off at the crossing we figger there could be no better time for it to happen; so saddling up our private ponies us two boys and the cook set out for the crossing forty miles away. Too bad the ranch hands couldn't come, being they had to shovel so much hay *every day*, no more and no less, but they was good enough to let the cook go, remarking that if they couldn't get away they wouldn't keep anybody else from it.

We covered that forty miles and got to the other end in plenty time for the big midnight feed. We had our ears all wrapped up to keep 'em from freezing off, but, along with the coyotes

My bronc was "high-lifed"—goes to bucking and near hooks me on
the corner of the stable as he goes by.

howling to the moon, we could hear old Darb a-see-sawing on his fiddle and somebody else calling the dance a half a mile before we reached the house.

Lights was in every room and the smoke was coming straight up through three different chimneys; so we spurred up our ponies and rode towards the stack yards where we turned 'em loose.

We just enters the house as we hear a "tag" dance announced and by the time our chaps, spurs, and extra clothes are took off it's half over, but not too late to tag a couple of hombres, take their ladies, and dance some till *we* got tagged ourselves. When the dance was through the blood was beginning to circulate some, and by the time we shook hands all around we was more than ready to help keep things cheerful.

Half the crowd was cow-punchers from everywhere, a few cowmen with their families, from the oldest down to the weaner (what was left in the bedroom but made itself heard now and again), then a few boys from town what sleighed over and brought a few girls along. There was about six men to each lady, and it was always a wonder to me how the supposed to be weaker sex could tire the men even at that, but they did, and the fatter they was the longer they stayed.

The big feed at midnight and specially that coffee was a life saver to most of us what come in late; and when the fiddler re-sumed his playing there was no quitting till daybreak. The ladies all disappeared then, and us boys would take the floor and go on with the stag dance; if "fire-water" was around that stag dance was apt to be kind of rough and end up in wrestling matches.

Games and tricks of all kinds are tried; none are easy but some are done, and when that lags down there may be two young fellers in the corner what'd been visiting the bottom of the manger too often and arguing or betting on riding; more bets are put in from the outside crowd just to make things interesting.

The bunch all heads for the corrals and a wall-eyed rangy bronc is led out, saddled, straddled, and with the bawling of that bronc bucking away with a whooping rider fanning him, the crowd hollering "stay with him, cowboy" or the like, the sun is coming up, the ladies are waking, and the end of the doings have come.

Breakfast is spread and all hands, after partaking of the bait, are talking of hitting the trail. Ponies are caught, harnessed or saddled, and with a lot of howdedo the crowd is leaving for their home grounds.

My bronc was "high-lifed" as I go through the corral gate and bucks right through the calf pen, same as it wasn't there, near hooking on the corner of the stable as he goes by; but a mile further on he cools down some and the boys catch up with me.

We're riding along a ways, when Dan remarks, "I feel something in the air." A light breeze had sprung up from the west, and come to think about it, it felt a whole lot as if a chinook was headed our way, and as we ride on that breeze keeps a-getting warmer and stronger. The deep snow was already beginning to show the effects and sagging as the warm wind et its way through.

The next day as I ride out of camp the chinook is blowing for sure, and when I strikes the first bunch of cattle I found them to be as I was afraid I would.   They'd been strong and rustling fine a few days before; they'd been on their feet steady through the cold weather, not hankering to lay down in the snow, and the exercise kept the blood circulating; but the chinook had took

"Tailing up" is mighty hard, and the critter is never grateful.

the snow off a few spots on the ridges and at them spots is where I finds most of the stock laying down and all the life out of 'em.

They was hardened to the cold and the sudden warmth left 'em so weak that only half of 'em can get up as I rides in on 'em.   I spends a couple of hours helping the weakest ones by "tailing 'em up," and steadying 'em some afterwards so they can navigate.   I'm working hard 'cause I know that when the chinook quits blowing and it gets cold again them cattle what are down now will get stiff and cramped, the blood'll quit circulating, and the critters' legs will be plumb useless, which leaves 'em good only for coyote bait.

"Tailing up" is an awful hard and ungrateful job too, the critter treats you the same as if you was a bear or a wolf what's come to eat her alive, and proceeds to try and hook you, and, wild-eyed, bellers in your ear how she'd like to tear you up. You help her along and she struggles to get on her feet, not so that she might be able to rustle and live but just to get a chance to run you down. Sometimes she works hard enough that she forgets what she was going to do when she did get on footing again, and if you can sneak away using her body to keep her from seeing you and get on your horse before she sees, everything may be O. K.; but, if she happens to turn her head and glance back as you're making your getaway, she might remember what she wanted to do to you a while ago *and try it*. She'll let out a bellering war whoop and forget that she's kinda shaky in the knees, and is apt to turn and try to get to you too quick, which makes her do a spraddling nose dive. Down again, and there to stay unless you help her up once more and make a success of your getting away.

I've tailed up one critter as often as half a dozen times before I could leave without her taking after me and falling down again. Then I'd have to hang my coat (when I had one with me) over her horns and blindfold her that way till I'd get to my horse. Once in the saddle I'd ride by her, get the coat back and be away before she'd know what happened.

Well, I kept a-riding the bare ridges that day and getting cattle on their feet and moving. The next day was the same and the chinook was still a-blowing and eating up the snow. Half of it is already melted away and water is running down the coulees to the creeks, making 'em the size of rivers. Any stranger would of thought sure that spring'd come sudden, but I knowed the cowmen was losing sleep for worrying, more afraid of the harm the hard freeze would do to the stock after the chinook'd left than the chinook itself could do while it was blowing.

Along about the middle of the afternoon I meets with the other rider; I sees he's near all in as he pulls up his horse and goes to rolling a smoke, but he's smiling some as he remarks that these winter jobs sure do get aggravating at times. We had pretty well all of our cattle up and a-going again and it was about time, 'cause we could feel the air getting cooler and the breeze was shifting to the north. The snow'd quit melting and the creeks was getting down to creek size again. "I'm thinking to-night is going to put a crimp in some of the stock," Dan says as we start out for some draws to the west where we figgered to find the few bunches of cattle we'd missed in our circles.

It's good and dark by the time we head our horses towards camp and it was getting colder every minute. The wet snow was freezing through solid and in lots of places the top crust would hold our horses. "I wouldn't be surprised," I says, "but what the Old Man (meaning the superintendent) might have to either ship the stock south to pull 'em through the winter, that is if they can make it to the railroad, or else ship some feed in and haul it out here to 'em; that would be some expensive too. The bad shape the range is in now with all the good feed buried in solid ice, something'll sure have to be done or else the outfit'll find itself with more cowboys than cattle when spring does come."

"Sure," Dan says, "and for my part I wouldn't mind hitting south with the stock 'cause I feel like I could stand some warmer climate myself." And rubbing his ears he puts his horse into a lope remarking that we'd better be drifting if we want anything to eat that's warm.

The Cypress Cattle Company was running over thirty thousand head of cattle; three thousand of 'em was at Stone Pile camp, where Dan and me was riding, the rest was at other cow camps, and a big herd at the home ranch, where there was other riders and hay shovellers looking after 'em. At our camp there was enough hay put up the summer before to feed and pull through the winter about fifteen hundred head of stock. The other fifteen hundred was supposed to rustle. They could easy enough and come out strong in the spring after any average winter, 'cause the stock what was left out on the range to rustle through was all dry stuff and steers. Cows with calves and weaners and all old or weak stock was fed from the start of the bad weather till spring breakup.

The weather kept clear and cold; the little glass tube outside our camp by the door was saying from thirty to thirty-five below, and had been keeping that up for about a week. Lucky, we thought, the wind wasn't blowing then or every critter would of froze stiff where they stood. We kept on bringing in the weak-

I can see by the signs in the snow where she'd stopped and made a stand.

est and only them what really needed feed the most. There was many more should been brought in but the last week made us fill the feed yards, so that it wouldn't be wise to bring them in. There was enough hay to feed fifteen hundred head till spring and it was better, we thought, to keep on feeding just them and take a chance on letting the stronger pull through on the outside, than feed two thousand or more and run out of hay at the wrong time and lose 'em all.

It didn't look like there was going to be any shipping done either way. No super or cow boss showed up to see how the stock was coming and we figgered that old timers like they was, and never forgetting the days when there wasn't a hoof fed, they'd decided to take a chance like they'd done many a winter before and hope that the weather would change in some way in time to save the stock. And as luck would have it the weather did change.

It was near three weeks since the chinook'd come and left the range a field of ice and crusted snow with the few bare spots that helped some keeping the cattle alive. The willows on the creek bottoms and the sage was all et down to the ice, and, outside of the few branches what was too big for them to tackle, the country was clean as a whistle. There was little bunches of range horses here and there and even though they was having a hard time of it, it was some easier for them 'cause they could paw out their feed where the critter could only root with her nose. But along the trails the horses would make where they pawed up the hard snow and broke the crust with their hoofs, you could see the cattle following and picking what the horses would leave.

Big hunks of crusted snow had been pawed out and turned up for the feed underneath, but as they was loosened the grass came out with the hunks and left only bare ground.

The stock had so little feed in 'em that it looked like their flanks was near touching the backbone, but the most of 'em was strong and if it hadn't been for that chinook they would now be in good shape.

Anyway the weather changed and for the best. We didn't think it for the best at first 'cause the change was for *another chinook* and they as a rule don't leave nothing but bone piles unless they come late in the spring, and this was only February. For forty-eight hours it blowed warm. Dan and me was doing our bestest riding, and tailing up for all we was worth every critter what had to be helped on her feet. We'd remark that it'd be for the last time 'cause we was sure afraid of what the cold that 'most always follows a chinook would do to 'em.

It started clouding up before the chinook quit, and that's when our hopes come back. The snow was 'most all gone to water and running down the draws; the country was left bare and brown and the cattle weaker than ever, but feed a-plenty was in sight and easy to get at, and clouding up as it was with the wind dying down gives us to understand that there won't be no real cold weather coming right soon anyway.

It stayed warm and in a couple of days it started to snow, kinda wet at first, but she stuck and kept on a-coming, slow but sure and steady. The cloudy weather was with us for a good two weeks and gradually getting colder, when it cleared again and the thermometer went down to ten below. There was near

My horse don't quite agree to all the load and specially objects
to wolves.

a foot of snow on the ground again and the cattle was having a hard time rooting down to the feed, but the slow drop of the thermometer and the chance at some feed before the snow came recuperated 'em some. A few more had to be brought in and we did it, taking big chances of running out of hay too soon.

And then another six inches of snow piled up on top of the foot already down, which makes us and the hay shovellers do a heap of figgering as to how we was going to pull the stock through. The hay was fed and handled real careful but it was dwindling away fast; two thousand of the hungry critters was in the feed pens eating up the hay what was supposed to carry not over fifteen hundred head.

And by all appearances it looked like the "hospital stuff" would have to be fed another six weeks before we could call 'em pulled through. Dan and me was doing our darnedest not to bring in any more than we could help and coaxing 'em along to stand up and rustle where they was, but there was times right along every day when we'd have to come in with a few more.

Spring was late, it still looked like the middle of winter, and we had to contend not only with the usual few winter calves but spring calves was beginning to pop up here and there and showing their little white faces. The daggone coyotes was the only animal getting fat, and it sure used to do my heart a lot of good to keel one of 'em over just when he'd be doing some tall sneak on some poor little feller of a calf when his mammy was too far away or too weak to get there in time to do any protecting.

Like one day riding along and keeping tab on the weak ones as usual, I runs across a cow-track in the snow. A little baby calf was trying mighty hard to keep up with her and a little further on there's two other kinds of tracks joins in and follows. They're big tracks, too big for coyotes, and I concludes they must be gray wolves. Now I know that as a rule wolves wouldn't tackle them only maybe just for the want to kill, or when horses is getting scarce.

Anyway, I know *I* sure like to get 'em *any time I can* no matter what they're after, and spurs up on the trail, the 30-30 carbine right in my hands and the business end of it pointed straight ahead. Daggone 'em, they *are* after that cow and calf. I can see that plain enough by the signs in the snow where she'd stopped, made a stand and went on for some place (I figgered) where she could back up alongside a cliff or something and have only one side to watch from.

I can see the wolves are only after a little excitement 'cause they could of killed both her and the calf right there and then if they'd wanted to. Instead, they just let her go and kept on aggravating her as she went. I thought to myself if they're so rearing for excitement, I'd sure be glad to oblige 'em that way when I catches up.

The trail heads on for the foot-hills; I'm keeping my horse into a high lope, and slacks up only when topping ridges, so I won't bump into the little party and queer things before I can get into action. I want to see them before they see me.

I finally spots 'em a half a mile to the right. There's a ridge between us, and soon as I get a peek of their whereabouts and the lay of the land, what little I showed of myself is out of sight again. I seen where the mother'd found a good spot to make

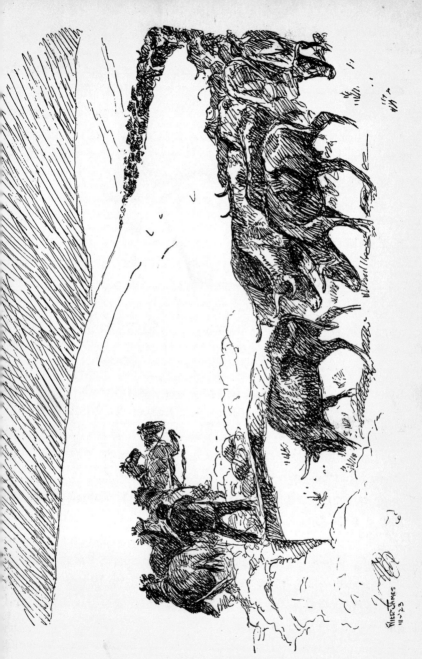

It wasn't but a few days when the cattle all knowed what them V-shaped logs dragging along meant.

her *last stand*, and, even tho' she knowed how the fight was going to end, she was sure making use of the rim-rock she'd backed up against, and bellering for help that didn't seem to come.

Hell bent for election I follows up the draw I'm in to where I figger I'd better hoof it the rest of the way. There was no wind to give me away, and I manages to crawl up to within fifty yards of the fighting bunch, taking in at a glance all what'd been going on while I'm looking down the rifle sights.

The wolves are enjoying themselves so much that they're not on the look-out as they generally are. They had the cow down and letting her last as long as they could without allowing the fight to get too monotonous. Her head and horns are still a-going and mighty dangerous to anything what comes near. The poor little calf was all together as yet, and off a ways, plumb helpless and watching, too young to know for sure what to do. The wolves had figgered him not worth while to fool with right then. They'd fix his mammy first, spend a few minutes with him afterwards, and then go on to the next victim.

And right there I stopped one of 'em with a bullet right through him from shoulder to shoulder. The other started to run and I lets him have a pill too, but he kept on a-running, dragging two useless hind legs; his back was broke. A couple more shots what don't seem to affect him none and I gets my horse, takes after him, and brings him back, limp, with a bullet between his ears.

I gathers up little Johnny (calf), puts his dying mammy out of misery, and being I'm not very far from camp, I don't stop to skin the wolves right then but takes 'em in as they are. Tying their hind legs together I throws 'em over the back of the saddle, gets on myself and pulls the little "leppy" up in front of me. My horse don't quite agree to all the load and specially objects to wolves, but I finally talks him into being good enough to take us the little ways to camp.

Two more weeks gone, and it still looks and feels like the middle of winter, when by rights of season the range ought to be getting bare of snow and the grass showing a little green; and worse yet, the hay is all gone and fed up, every speck of it.

There was a little horse hay, but that little bit wouldn't mean nothing to all them hungry cattle, and besides them horses had to work and help save them same cattle, and they had to be well fed to do that work.

So it seems to us that the outfit is up against it for sure. We know that no hay can be bought nowheres around, being they've all got their own stock to save and running short themselves. Dan and me had just about give up thinking of some way out, when of a sudden it comes to me, and I remembers of how one time up in Alberta a cowman saved his stock and pulled 'em through in good shape with a six-horse team and a drag (or snowplough).

No more thought of than tried. There was enough harness in the stables to hook up thirty head of horses, and two teams on hand and ready; but we wanted two six-horse teams to do the work and we was short eight head; so Dan and me hits out looking through every bunch of horses on the range for anything what had collar marks, and any of 'em what had was run in and put to work. It didn't matter whether they belonged to the outfit or not.

Two V-shaped drags was made out of heavy logs with thick planks nailed on the outside so it'd push the snow away on both sides and clean. We get the teams all hooked up, straightened around, and we're ready to go. It worked fine, and the grass wherever we went and drug was easy to get. The snow hadn't drifted any and was no thicker in the draws than on the ridges, so we worked the draws and found plenty of the good strong feed our cattle was needing so bad.

We had to cover a lot of country and keep a-going so that they'd all get some; but the exercise and rustling, along with that feed they was getting, made 'em some stronger, and it wasn't but a few days when the cattle all knowed what them V-shaped logs dragging along meant.

The strongest ones would follow 'em right up for a ways, and we'd come down the same draw but on the other side. The leaders would stop and feed, leaving the weaker cattle have a chance as we come by.

That'd been going on for about two weeks; the stock wasn't picking up no fat but they was making out all right. The ranch-hands handled the drags and Dan and me was riding, still bringing a few weak ones from the outside stuff every once in a while.

May was getting near now and sure enough spring ought to show itself pretty quick if it's going to show up at all; but as Dan remarked to me and says, "Bill, this damn country ain't got no spring or summer to speak of; it's eight months winter and four months cold weather," and I begins to think he was right.

But the days was getting longer and the sun stronger, and

pretty soon it begins to get warmer, and after a while I notices at the edge of where the snow'd been scraped of that the grass was getting green. It looked so good that I come near eating some.

Then one morning as I'm saddling up, a light breeze hits me, and it's coming from the southwest. After that it didn't take long; it started to melt and get warm but not so warm that it'd weaken the cattle too much. The snow-plough was put away and instead of bringing in weak stock any more we'd spend our time tailing up what few felt the effects of the coming warm weather.

We was beginning to see little white and brockle-faced calves sunning themselves everywhere and their mammies right close was filling up on the half green buffalo grass, picking up steady on fat and strength.

The gray wolves was hitting out for the tall timber and the coyotes had to be satisfied with gophers once more.

Spring had come.

THE MAKINGS OF A
COW-HORSE

CHAPTER VI

A MONTH or so before the round-up wagons pull out, the raw bronc (unbroke range horse) is enjoying a free life with the "stock horses" (brood-mares and colts). He's coming four years old marked by the first signs of spring. A few warm days starts him shedding, and just as the green grass is beginning to peek out from under the snow and living is getting easier, why here comes a long lanky rider on a strong grain-fed horse and hazes him and the bunch he's with into the big corrals at the home-ranch.

He's cut out with a few more of his age and put into a small round corral — a snubbing post is in the centre — and showed where, according to the rope marks around it, many such a bronc as him realized what they was on this earth for.

The big corral gate squeaks open and in walks the long lanky cowboy packing two ropes; one of them ropes sneaks up and snares him by the front feet just when he's making a grand rush to get away from it. He's flattened to the ground and that other rope does the work tying him down. A hackamore is slipped on his head while the bronc is still wondering what's happened, and from the time he's let up for a sniff at the saddle he's being eddicated, so that when the wagon pulls out a few weeks later his first promotion comes, and he's classed as "saddle-stock."

From then it's 'most all up to what kind of a head that pony's got whether he'll get on further than being just a saddle-horse. He may have to be pulled around a lot to get anything out of him towards what he should do, or on the other hand, he may take to it easy and get down to learning of his own accord after his bucking spells are over with.

He'll get all the time he needs to catch onto the new ropes of cow work, and only one thing at a time will be teached to him so that he'll not be rattled, but first, his bucking is what the rider'll object to and try to break him out of, and every time he bogs his head for that perticular kind of orneriness that bronc is apt to get his belly-full of the quirt.

But the cow-foreman has no place on the outfit he's running for any such hombre what don't treat the ponies right, and if a cowboy is kept on the pay-roll what naturally is rough on horse-flesh he'll get a string of horses cut to him that's just as mean as he is and fight him right back, or even go him one better whenever the chance shows up.

There's horses though that has to be rough handled, born fighters what'll do just the opposite of what they should do to be good; they want to be ornery and them kind calls only for the real rough bronco fighter what'll fight 'em to a finish.

Them's the kind of horses what makes up a "rough-string"; every cow outfit has 'em. Them horses'll range in age from five-year-old colts what craves fighting on up to fifteen and twenty-year-old outlaws; they 'most always keep one man in the hospital steady, and when he comes out the other man is about due to take his place either with the nurses or the angels.

One of them ropes sneaks up and snares him by the front feet just when he's making a grand rush to get away from it.

SANTA CLARA COUNTY FREE LIBRARY
SAN JOSE, CALIF.

The good, patient "bronc twister" what takes pains to teach the bronc to be good and be a real cow-horse don't as a rule have anything to do with the "rough-string"; his patience and ability with horses is too valuable to the company to have it go to waste on outlaws. So his work comes in on the uneddicated colt (the raw bronc), trying in all ways to hold the good what's in him, at the same time keeping his spirit intact, and talk him out of being ornery, if he can.

Like for instance, that long lanky cowboy and the raw bronc I mentioned in the first part of this writing; they both have a mighty good chance of getting along fine with one another. If they do, that same bronc'll be rode out on circle and learn the ways of the critter, when later on he'll be turned over to another hand. The older cowboy, what's past hankering for "rough edges" on them broncs, will then take him and proceed to ride and help him along with his learning.

Then's when the good or the bad in him will come out to stay; at that time he knows the human enough to tell what to expect, and if he wants to be good he's got a mighty good chance, the same if he wants to be bad, for this older hand is not hankering to get in no mix-up; the pony feels that, and *if* he's bad at heart he'll sure take advantage of it and buffalo the older cowboy to turning him loose or else buck him off in the hills somewhere.

If he succeeds in running his bluff once he'll feel sure that he can do it with every man what tries to handle him, and if he can fight wicked enough it might be hard to show him different. Consequences is, if that confidence ain't taken out of him right sudden it'll take hold on him with the result that he lands in the "rough-string" and the promotion stops there, — one more what has to be tied down before he can be saddled.

But, being as I said before that this raw bronc and the long

I gave him a good half-hour to think it over.

lanky cowboy had mighty good chances of getting along fine, I'll let the good win out the same as it did with this perticular little horse I been trying to write about ever since I started this.

This little horse weighed around eleven hundred pounds and all in one hunk; what I mean is each part of him knowed what the other part was going to do and followed up according, without a kink nowheres. In bucking, or running, he'd make you wonder if he was horse-flesh or dynamite. Just an ordinary horse to look at though, chunky, short back and short ankles, but with a deep chest, and that head promised a lot either way he went.

That day I run him in, throwed him, and slipped the hackamore on his head, a name for him came to me just as natural as though I'd been thinking of one for hours. "Brown Jug," and that sure fit him all the way through even to the color; also like the jug he had plenty of "kick" in him.

From the first saddling he didn't disappoint me none, for he went after me and sure made me ride; in order to stay I had to postpone fanning him for a spell and thought I was doing real well to be able to do that much. It was just my luck that none of the boys was around to see me put up such a ride on such a horse; I told 'em about it, but, to the way it struck me, that was mighty tame compared to how it really was, and the next day when some of them boys happened around just as I was climbing Brown Jug again, the little son of a gun just crowhopped around and acted like he loved me and my rigging 'most to death.

He bucked at every setting each day after that for about ten days; then one day as I was going through the corral gate to give him his daily "airing," he "went to pieces" right there at the gate, and where it was slick with ice he fell hard and flat on his side and smashed one of my stirrups.

Naturally the first thing came to my mind was to hold him down for a spell and see if I was caught anywheres in the rigging. I wasn't. Then I thinks that now would be a good time to teach *his kind* of a horse how bucking wasn't at all nice, so I proceeds to tie him down. That don't hurt a horse, only his feelings, specially so when interrupted that way in the middle of the performance.

I'd whipped him some while bucking a few days before and I found out before I was through that his kind had to be handled different, 'cause he bucked and showed fight all the way through and never let up till he was tired out, then he went to sulking. After that I watched my chance for some other way to break him out of it.

My chance came when he fell and I didn't let it slip by. I gave him a good half-hour to think it over, and when I let him up, me a-setting in the saddle, he was glad to get away from the forced rest and be able to stand on his pins again; but he was sure took down a peg, and when I loped him out sudden he seemed to've forgot that was the time he liked to buck best.

There was twelve broncs in my string, each was getting short rides on "inside circle," or at the cutting grounds. Their teaching came right along with the cattle and the average of them colts was coming fine, but Brown Jug was ahead of 'em all and naturally I helped him all the more.

He'd bucked only once since I tied him down and that second time he didn't get to buck like he wanted to then; he'd only made a half a dozen jumps, when I reached down on one rein, pulled his head up and jerked his feet out from under him, laying him down again just when he wanted to be in action the most.

That fixed him for good, and I figgered if he'd ever buck again it'd be when he got cold and wanted to warm up, or when somebody'd tickle him with the spur at the wrong time. Well, if he did it'd only show he had feelings and the kind of spirit that makes the cow-horse.

It was a couple of weeks since Brown Jug'd bucked last; it was out of his system by now and I was beginning to take a lot of interest in the ways of handling the critter. I kept him in my string long as I could; then one day the foreman, who'd been watching with an eagle eye the work of every colt I'd been break-ing, figgered the "raw edge" was pretty well took off them broncs and fit to be divided up amongst the boys for easy work.

The next morning I'm ready to leave the wagon behind, also the ponies I'd broke, and hit back for the home-ranch on a gentle horse, where I'm to round up another string of raw broncs and start in breaking fresh. But before leaving I manages to get the foreman to one side. "Now Tom," I says, "there's one special little horse in them broncs I'm turning over what has the makings of a 'top-horse' and I'd sure like to see a real good man get him, a man that'll make him what he promises to be. I know Flint Andrews would sure like to have him, and I'm asking as a favor if you'd see that Flint gets Brown Jug."

"You surprise me, Bill," he says, squinting over Brown Jug's way, then back at me, "why I thought all horses was alike to you no matter how good or bad they be; but I guess I thought wrong, and if you'd like to see Flint get the brown horse don't worry about it, he'll get him."

"That's the trouble being a bronc peeler and working for them big cow outfits," I says to my horse as I'm riding along back to the ranch; "a feller don't no more than begin to get interested in the way the colts are learning; and just about the time the orneriness is took out of 'em and they're behaving fine they're took away and scattered along in the other boys' strings, and another bunch of green, raw, fighting broncs takes their place."

I'm at the ranch near three weeks and coming along pretty fair with the new bunch when the wagons begin pulling in. The spring round-up was over with, and three of the four "remudas" was being corralled one after another; cow-horses, night-horses, and circle-horses was being cut out and turned on the range to rest up till the next spring, over five hundred head of 'em, and the other two hundred was put in the pasture to keep going till fall round-up. Them was the colts what'd just been "started" that spring along with the "spoiled horses" what belonged most to the "rough-string," and needed steady setting on in order to make 'em good.

Brown Jug came in with one of the remudas and was looking fine, Flint couldn't get to me quick enough to tell me what a great little horse he was, and how near he could come to being human. "Never kettled (bucked) once," he says, "and I never saw a horse getting so much fun out of beating a critter at her own game as he does; he sure camps on their hocks from start to finish."

A few days later I had a chance to watch him at work. Flint was a-talking away to him and that little son of a gun of a horse seemed to understand everything he said and talk right back with them ears and eyes of his. I was getting jealous of what Flint could do with Brown Jug, and it set me down a peg to see that he sure had me beat in teaching him something. I was

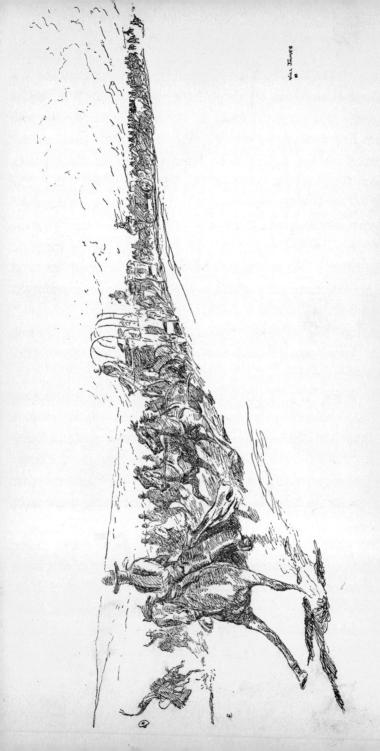

Two more such outfits was to start out soon for other directions and on other ranges.

alright when it come to starting a colt and taking the rough off him, but after that I sure had to take a back seat from Flint.

The boys was rounding up fresh horses and the wagons was getting ready to pull out again, all the corrals was being used and every rider was topping off the horses cut to him; from ten to fifteen head of the big fat geldings is what made a "string," and the company saw that each cowboy had all he needed far as horse-flesh was concerned.

And when the four and six horse teams was hooked on the "chuck," "bed," and "wood" wagons and the big corral gates was opened to let the remuda follow, every cowboy was on hand and ready. "The pilot" (rider piloting the wagon through the roadless plains and breaks) started, the cook straightened out his team and followed with the chuck wagon, then the "flunky" next with the bed wagon, and the "nighthawk" (night herder for the saddle-horses) on the wood wagon took up the swing, then last came the day wrangler bringing up the rear with upward of two hundred head of saddle stock, the remuda.

Fifteen or more of us riders rode along the side, doing nothing in perticular but keeping our ponies right side up till we come to the country where the work begins. The whole outfit moved on a fast trot and sometimes going down a sag you could see the cook letting his team hit out on a high lope, and the rest was more than aching to keep up.

Two more such outfits was to start out soon for other directions and on other ranges. I went along with the first; the broncs I'd just started a few weeks before was in the remuda and on the trail of eddication to the ways of the critter, the same as the bunch I'd took along early that spring.

In this new string of broncs I was putting through the ropes, there was another special little horse what promised to come up along with Brown Jug as a cow-horse. But I was kinda worried, he was *too* good, never bucked once and seemed to try too hard to learn. His kind of a horse was hard for me to make out, 'cause they was few. I always felt they was waiting for a chance to get you, and get you good whenever that chance showed up.

I figgered a horse with a good working set of brains like he had ought to've done *something*, but all he did do was to watch me like a hawk in every move I'd make; and he was so quiet when I was around that I naturally felt kind of nervous, thinking he might explode and tear up the scenery 'most any minute.

But he stayed good and kept a-learning fast, and even though I figgered he might be one example of a horse in a thousand, I was still dubious when I turned him and a few others of my broncs over to the boys. I wished he'd bucked, once anyway.

I kept my eye on him, and every time it was his turn to be rode I was always surprised to see how docile he was. The new hand what was riding him made an awful fuss over "Sundown," as he'd called him (he was too much of a puzzle for *me* to name) and the two was getting along better than I ever expected.

With Brown Jug, he was showing a little orneriness now and again, but that was to be expected, and Flint could 'most always talk him out of it. He done the work though, and was getting so he could turn a "bunch-quitting" critter so fast she'd think she was born that way.

And, if you'd asked me right quick which one of them two ponies, Brown Jug or Sundown, would make the best cow-horse I'd said Brown Jug; on the other hand, if you'd let me think it over for a spell it'd been that to my way of thinking that the two horses don't compare; they're both working fine, but I trust Brown Jug and I can't as yet trust Sundown. Anyway, to put myself in the clear I'd said "let's wait and see."

My broncs being all took away but four, a string of "cut," "circle," and "night" horses are turned over to me and I gets in on circle day-herd and night-guard with the rest of the boys, so now I can watch the colts I'd started get their finished eddi-cation.

Fall was coming on and the air was getting crimpy; the light frosts was turning the grass to brown, and the old ponies was developing a hump in their backs and had to have their bucking space to warm up in before straightening out and tending to business.

For the good old honest hard-working cow-horse does buck, and buck mighty hard sometimes, specially on cold mornings, but he's never "scratched" for it. The cowboy a-setting atop of him will only grin at the perticular way the pony has of un-limbering for the work what's ahead of him on the "cutting grounds." He'll be talked to a lot and kidded along for his "crooked ways," while he's tearing up the earth and trying to be serious in his bucking, and never will either the quirt or the spur touch that pony's hide while he's acting on that way, for him being a cow-horse and at the top of the ladder in saddle stock gives him a lot of privilege.

The cow-horse I'm speaking of here is the *real one*, the same you'd find anywheres, some years ago, even to-day on the big cow outfits to the east of the Rockies and on the plateaus stretching from Mexico to Canada. This cow-horse done nothing but cow work where it'd need a pony of his kind. He never was rode out on circle or straight riding and never was used anywheres outside of on the cutting grounds. All the action, strength, endurance, and intelligence that pony has was called for *there*, and the horse that could do that work and do it well was worth near his weight in gold to the country.

I well remember the time, and not so long ago, when you could buy any amount of mighty good saddle-horses for from five to twenty dollars a head, well-reined horses that could turn a Sonora "yak" quicker than you could wink; and I'll leave it to any cowman what savvies them cattle that that's saying a lot. But there was something them same ponies lacked to make 'em real cow-horses; what they lacked was intelligence, knowing where to be ahead of time when the snaky critter side-winded here or there, and put 'er out of the "main herd" before she had time to double back. Them same ponies depended too much on the touch of the rein; they couldn't see themselves what they should do, and far as they'd get in saddle stock was "dayherd," "circle," or "rope horse."

Where with the real cow-horse, he's the kind what'll work *with* the man, he's got to be able to see what should be done and do it without waiting for the feel of the rein, for sometimes things are done so quick in working a herd or cutting out a critter that the human eye or hand may be too slow, and that's

All that could be got of him was buck, fight, sulk, and stampede.

where the instinct of the cow-horse comes in, to pick up the slack. He's got brains enough to know what the cowboy wants done, and he goes ahead and does it.

Man is not all responsible for making the cow-horse what he is; you got to give the pony half the credit, for after all, man only shows him the work and coaches him along some, but the horse himself does that work and will take enough interest in it as to sometimes bite a hunk of rawhide and beef right off some critter's rump if that critter happens to act ornery.

You can see feelings and wisdom all over that pony as he winds in and out through the herd. He goes along with his head straight from the body, not paying no attention to any of the bellering herd around him. The cowboy leaves the reins hanging loose and then, of a sudden the horse is given a sign which is really *no sign at all*, but anyway the pony knows *somehow* that the rider has a critter located and to be cut out; and even though there may be some cattle between him and that certain critter, he has a strong hunch just which one it is; that's enough for the cow-horse to work on.

Such a horse couldn't be bought at all, and many a time I've seen two hundred dollars or more (that was a lot of money then) offered and turned down for the likes, when the other well-reined kind could be got in trade for only a saddle blanket or a box of cartridges. Yessir, you'd had to buy the whole kaboodle, cattle, horses, range, and all, in order to get the cow-horse I'm speaking of here.

And Brown Jug, he was turning out to be just that kind of a horse. That fall after his first summer of eddication with the cow, he showed strong where in a couple more years he'd be a top cow-horse, the kind what's talked about around the cow camps from the Rio Grande to the Yellowstone. Flint was always raving about him and I'd always chip in with "well, look who started him."

Sundown was coming up right along with Brown Jug, and the new hand what was riding him sure used to get into some long sizzling arguments with Flint over them two ponies, but the argument kept neck to neck, same as it did with the horses.

They was both turned out that fall together with the rest of the remuda. That winter was easy on all stock, and the horses was all packing a big fat when spring broke up.

The spring horse round-up brought in near a thousand head of saddle stock, and in one of the corrals with other horses I got first glimpse of Brown Jug and Sundown. They'd been pals all winter and where one went the other followed; if one got into a scrap the other helped him and they sure made a dandy pair.

Flint'd been complaining of getting old and stiff for a week or so past, and when he seen Brown Jug acting snorty he mentioned it again, and a little stronger this time. Finally I took the hint and told him I'd top him off for him if he wanted me to. "Sure," he says, "I don't mind."

Well sir, that little horse gave me a shaking up the likes I never had before or since, and when he finally quit and I got off, I was beginning to feel old and stiff myself, but I rode him again that afternoon and took it out of him easy enough. The next day he was all right and Flint rode him away.

After he put a couple of boys in the hospital and come damn near getting me, he was put in the "rough-string."

In another corral something was more than raising the dust, and soon as I see what causes it, I don't lose no time to climb the poles and get there. Sundown had "broke in two" *at last*. The new hand was having it out with him but he had no chance.

That little horse without man or bridle puts 'er out of the herd, and heads 'er for the cut.

Somehow he stayed on though and when the horse quit he fell off like a rag.

I takes a turn at that horse and tired as he is he sure makes it interesting, and I don't find no time to use the quirt. He finally quits again and I was mighty glad of it. He's standing with legs wide apart, fire in his eyes and puffing away like a steam-engine and when I tries to move him out of his tracks, all

I gets is a couple more hard stiff jolts. He's mad clear through and I know there's no use trying to make him do anything just then.

From then on he was just as bad this spring as he was good the spring before. All that could be got of him was buck, fight, sulk, and stampede. He was no more interested in anything else, and after he put a couple of boys in the hospital and come damn near getting me, he was put in the "rough-string."

I wasn't surprised to see him turn out that way; if anything, I kind of expected it. For even though I've seen a *few* what never bucked on first setting and stayed good all the time, I always figgered there was something wrong with 'em and could never trust 'em till I knowed for sure.

I quit the outfit that year, right after the spring round-up was over, and it was a couple of years later when I rode back into that country. The spring round-up was in full swing and a herd was being "worked" a little ways from camp.

I rides over, and there was Flint and Brown Jug working *together*, and doing the prettiest job of cutting out I ever saw. A long-legged and long-horned staggy-looking critter was being edged to the outside of the herd, and I could see that critter had no intentions of being put out of that herd, none at all.

Pretty soon an opening shows up, and Brown Jug come pretty near seeing it quicker than Flint. Anyway that critter was stepped on from there and put out before she knowed it. She tries to turn back, but the little horse was right on hand at each side step, when of a sudden Brown Jug stumbles. His foot had gone down a badger hole and he come near turning over. Flint quits him, and when the little horse straightens up the bridle is off his head. All was done quicker than you could think and the critter hadn't had time to get back to the herd.

Then, Brown Jug sees 'er, and, transformed into a lightning streak, he lands on 'er; the fur is flying off that critter's rump and that little horse without man or bridle keeps on as though nothing happened and puts 'er out of the herd and heads 'er for the cut.

Nobody says anything for a spell, but the expressions means a lot. Then the foreman, who'd seen it all, kinda grins and says: "If I had a few more horses like that I wouldn't need no men."

A few days later that same foreman piles his rope on Brown Jug, leads him out, and puts his own saddle on him. That sure set me to thinking, for even the boss is not supposed to ride any horse the company furnishes you with in your string, and still wondering I looks over at Flint, who's leading out the boss's top horse and putting *his* saddle on him.

I finds out afterwards that they'd swapped, and that Flint was to get his wages raised to boot, but I could see that Flint wasn't any too happy over the trade and I says to him, "I guess you feel about the same now as I did when *I had* to turn him over to you three years ago."

"Yes," he answers, "and worse."

But even at that, we was both mighty proud that we'd helped make Brown Jug what he was, *the top cow-horse of four remudas.*

THE LONGHORNS

CHAPTER VII

WHEN we speak of the longhorns in the cow country, we most generally set back some, and think back a whole lot. And thinking, we sometimes wonder if the Spaniards realized when they brought the first of them cattle over from Spain that they was responsible for the good they done in stocking up the Southwest and making it the starting of the cow country it turned out to be.

It took a couple of hundred years for them first cattle to multiply and spread out, so that the whole of California and plum across to the Gulf of Mexico was cut up by the trails them roaming herds would make. There come a time when their trails run in with the buffalo's down in Texas; they drank of the same waters and grazed on the same flats. They changed some in build to fit in with what the country called for, and came right up with the buffalo in speed and endurance.

Then come a time when the pioneers what drifted in that country started claiming 'em, and the cattle got a *burning* feeling that they wasn't as free as before. Old Maverick claimed a good many and finally decided it'd be best to put a brand on his thousands of cattle, if he wanted to keep 'em *his*. That was before "irons" had to be recorded or before there was any such a place where you could record 'em at.

The long horned, long legged critters stayed wild and mighty spooky. They couldn't afford to pack extra fat as it'd hinder 'em in their running, and outside of keeping the few people in meat and supplying the markets with rawhide, they had nothing to do but run, accumulate, and stay wild.

They done all them things in fine style — but, all too soon (as some of the old cowmen will tell you) the railroads blazed a way towards the gold fields and other glittering facts the West held out for them who wanted to come and get it.

With the folks piling in sky high and more of 'em coming steady from acrost the ocean, it wasn't long till there was use for them buckskin cattle, and other than for the rawhide they was packing. The stockman what was already there ahead of the crowd started to keep better tab of his stock and finally got to thinking so much of 'em all of a sudden, that he'd just hang high and dry any one caught stealing any of them critters.

The cattle getting more handling and care naturally got more gentle and got so in time that you could keep sight of 'em and not even have to get your horse out of a lope; but in the thick brush or rocky countries, and wherever it was so rough that the riders rode around there was big herds stayed wild, and nobody seemed to want to fool with them just then.

But it wasn't so very long till they was pecked at, and come a time when instead of them wild bunches increasing as they should they was gradually dwindling down to a few. Them few was making themselves mighty hard to find though, and kept a-making such a good job of hiding away in their rough countries that they held their little bunches to near normal in size.

Only a half dozen years ago you could still run across a few of them wild ones right along with the wild horses, but there wasn't much if any of the old longhorn strain in 'em, for as the gentler range cattle down in the flats below was getting of the

I'd take my rope down and try my luck but that critter would leave
me as though I was standing still.

better breed and as some of them yearlings and two-year-olds was straying away and joining the wild bunch now and again, them strays would gradually kill the old strain and keep the wild ones up in breed.

But their wild instinct stayed the same, or if anything they got wilder and wiser, and I wouldn't be surprised if I was to ride along and still find a few of them wild unbranded critters even to-day. 'Cause the country they'd pick on to run in then hasn't changed much, if any, since, and as I've already said it was well out of the way of riders and no place to run high priced range cattle in.

Them wild ones scattered along up through the Rockies into the Northern States. And wherever you could find deer, elk, and mountain lions in the cow country was where you'd also find them wild "orejanas," but they was even harder to get a sight of than any deer. They'd always see you first and had the sage chicken beat when it come to hiding, they'd stand still as a petrified tree and let you ride past within a few yards of 'em if they thought they was well enough hid. But if there was no hiding place handy they'd take to running, and I never yet seen a horse that could catch up with 'em in their brushy, rocky territory.

I've seen 'em sometimes a little out in the open and where I thought I had a good running chance at 'em. I'd take my rope down and try my luck but that critter would leave me as though I was standing still, and hit out for the best goat country you ever saw, hardly ever breaking out of a long trot, the likes of which would sure make any mountain raised horse use all the fastest gaits he had, but there was no catching up to within roping distance of 'em.

Amongst them wild bunches you'd sometimes find near pure bred Herefords and Durhams what had turned wild from not getting enough handling or being missed out of the round-up for a couple of years, others had been let go when they was wanting to fight some rider what tried to turn 'em too quick, and that rider being too busy at the time to take the orneriness out of one of 'em just left her behind, or whichever way she wanted to go.

With the result that (like some humans) that critter thought she had somebody buffaloed for sure, and head high, pacing pretty, hits out for the tall, rough, and uncut to join the rest of the wild bunch.

Then, yearlings and two-year-olds would stray away, run across the outlaws, and follow 'em along the high steep trails. They'd get numerous, and there'd come a time when us riders would have to pack 30-30's and get 'em the best way we could till the hills was clean of 'em. They'd be hauled to the railroad in wagons, and with a bullet hole back of their ears.

In the Southern States like Texas, New Mexico, and Arizona was where the wild stuff stayed wild the longest. They had bigger and rougher scopes of country to run in than could be found further north, and they wasn't affected much by the upbreeding of the tamer herds. The reason was that for every one well bred critter what strayed away and joined 'em, there'd be two long horned "Sonora Reds" butting in and keeping up the old strain.

Them wise hombres would feed in the open from sundown till sun-up, tank up on water while it was still dark, and then hide in the thick brush all day long, never coming out till the sun went down again. Solid stockade traps was built now and again, and big hunks of salt was used for the bait, and after letting things lay quiet for a week or a month, or till the critters got over being suspicious and came regular to get their lick of the salt, a drive was made with the idea to corral the bunch just when they'd least expect it.

A few, mighty few, would be corralled in and the rest would make a snorting getaway, them few that'd get caught would also get away sooner or later, for the corral couldn't hold up against them stout necks very long, and they had a way of working with them horns of theirs that would tear up 'most anything.

The stockmen kept a-worrying and thinking of new ways to handle them outlaws and tame 'em down so they could be run with the herd-broke range cattle. Shooting 'em was a waste of meat and hauling 'em in to the local butcher shop didn't bring a satisfactory price, besides there was times when them same butcher shops would have more beef than they could sell, and shipping took longer than the meat could wait to be still good.

And what was worse yet, was that a lot of young stock strayed away and joined them wild bunches every year, and the stockman saw where he sure had to do something about it — so, worrying along on that subject a new scheme was hatched out, a scheme that might seem kind of cruel to folks what never had any dealings with range stuff, but I'm sure that with a little experience along that line, them same folks would agree that even if it was a little cruel, it was also *mighty necessary*.

Part of that scheme was, that after each cowboy had picked two ropes, one being tied on the back of the saddle for emergency, and mounted on the best rope-horse the outfit could hand 'em,

It was a big spotted bull, the kind what wouldn't let a small object like a horse and a man keep him from going straight ahead to where he was headed, and I happened to be in his way.

they'd line out, about twenty riders of the kind what savvied how to handle the whale-line in the thick brush.

Like one time when a big circle was made. I was with the bunch and by the cracking of the brush ahead once in a while we could tell that a few of the critters was stirred up and getting together. Our intentions was to keep 'em going straight but the snaky critters was leery of openings; they stuck along to where the brush was the thickest and we'd have to lean away down alongside our horse's neck to keep from getting pulled off by the thick branches. Even at that there was places them dag-gone cattle went through on a high lope and where a lone horse couldn't follow on a walk and we had to go around. All that time them wild ones kept on the run, and we sure had to do some tall travelling to keep track of their whereabouts.

We didn't have a chance to crowd 'em, but we kept man-œuvring around and riding till we had 'em near the little openings and then — things started to happen and we prepare for action. Not worrying about what limbs and stickers could do to our faces and hands we spur on full speed ahead, each cowboy with his hat pulled down hard a-squinting through his horse's ears and packing a "hungry loop." We form a circle around the "ore-janas" (unbranded cattle) before they know what's what and we've got 'em jammed in a small opening — but from all indi-cations they don't figger on us holding 'em there — and we don't, not no more than a second, but in that second we have enough time to each pick our victim.

They break through and by us in all directions, loops are spread out and circle around big longhorns, the slack is pulled up, and the steers are going one way while the ponies are going another. There's an awful commotion and mixture of dust, ropes, steers, ponies, and men. Hollering and laughing cowboys, bellering mad critters, and cracking branches all throwed in.

The critter that come my way and I tied onto was good enough to hit the end of the rope fast and wicked and bust hisself into a fine laying position. I takes advantage of it and ties him down right there, and quicker than you could wink I shakes down my other rope and prepares for another victim, sees one what's trying to get out of the entanglements and snares it. About that time, I feels myself going up about ten feet, makes a circle in the air, and come down in a catclaw bush; I gets a glimpse of my horse where he'd come down flat on his back, and then I see the cause of the whole upheaval making his getaway.

It was a big spotted bull, the kind what wouldn't let a small object like a horse and a man keep him from going straight ahead to where he was headed, and I happened to be in his way. But he don't get to go far even at that. Two ropes pile in on him at once from two other riders, one of them ropes snaps like a thread and sings by like a bullet, but it checked him some till another rope was layed in the place of it, and it wasn't long till he was stretched out like any common critter.

In the meantime my little horse had picked himself up and was holding his own against the critter I'd caught, and that critter outweighed him a good hundred pounds; my saddle was slipping and I scrambles out of the scratching catclaw bush just in time to pull 'er straight, gives the steer some slack, and then goes the other way, laying that critter down and tying 'er in good time.

The dust settles some and I glances over the little half a mile opening. I can only see about half of the boys who are tying down what they caught, and scattered along in the opening is somewheres around fifteen head of tied critters, but I can still hear the brush a-cracking, and, wondering if I can be of any help, rides into the thick of it.

A mile away is another and smaller opening, and there was the rest of the boys with more tied critters. The cow foreman was rolling a smoke and acted real satisfied with the catch we'd made; a little bit of a bow-legged hombre from Texas had went and broke the record by catching and tying three of the wild ones all about a mile apart, but none of us had done bad, for out of the twenty riders was twenty-four caught orejanas.

The foreman was sharpening his knife, the while remarking that a few more runs like this one would soon clean the range of the wild stuff. And when the operation is performed on them critters we'd caught and we leaves 'em free, it sure didn't take 'em long for 'em to reach the brush line again. But there they'd stop and mighty quick, turn around, and paw the earth; something had gone wrong, and somehow or other they'd took a dislike to that thick brush where they used to hide and run so well. They tried to make cover a few times while we rode by headed back for camp, but each time they'd have to turn back and wild-eyed stare at us till we got out of sight.

"It might be a few days before they can work their way out and on the big flat with the other cattle" the boss remarked as we rode on, "but they'll be there to get their water, and once they're out of this brush all the cowboys in the world couldn't drive 'em back in."

Sure enough, in a few days they was out of the brush and mixing along with the other range stuff. They'd lost all hankering for anything but the big open flats, and even though they was wild as ever we had 'em where they'd soon tame down.

We made a few more runs and finally cleaned that range of all the wild stuff, putting 'em where they'd have to be good and to stay. The hardest part was catching 'em; after that it was easy, all we did was to cut their eyelids so they couldn't close their eyes.

Them eyelids being took from 'em and leaving their eyes unprotected not only made 'em lose their liking for the thick brush, but it also took the fight out of 'em, for in both places them same eyelids are mighty necessary if the critter wants to keep her eyesight; a twig don't feel good scraping along on a bare eye, and them critters knowed that without experimenting on it and kept out of trouble in that way. They picked up on fat and gradually lost their wild ideas and speed, and it wasn't long till they was just as contented in the big flats as they was in the brush where we'd got 'em out of.

When Old Mexico turned all upside down some years ago on account of the "paisanos" wanting more beans and maybe a little land of their own, the range there was well stocked up and full of the long horned cattle, and that country being on a rampage them cattle got to belonging to any of the Mexicanos

That ornery critter will find his head brought up right alongside his hind quarters.

or Yaquis who could by force and with saddle horses drive 'em off for keeps or to sell. But some of the "majordomos" got wise in time and beat the thieves to it by rounding up the stock fast as they could, and taking 'em across the line in the U. S., where they was sold to American cattle buyers, who turned 'em over to the cow outfits and scattered 'em all through the range countries plum up to Canada.

I well remember one year in the spring, when some of them long horned Mexico stuff was shipped north and turned loose in the river breaks and bad lands up there. There was about ten thousand head of 'em; when we unloaded 'em at the railroad they was mighty weak and mostly all head and horns from the suffering they'd went through in the country they'd just left.

They was trailed for a few hundred miles and turned loose amongst the gumbo and many-colored pinnacles, but there was feed a-plenty and the six months them cattle ranged in there sure made 'em hard to recognize both in looks and action. They hadn't seen a human in all that time and when I say they was wild just puts it kind of mild to what they really was.

When time come to round 'em up that fall, us boys was glad to find that there'd be very few drags in them, if any, and there wasn't. We'd ride the top of the ridges, let out a war whoop, fire a few shots from our six-shooters and them steers wasn't slow getting down into the draws. You could near hear their tails a-popping as they'd slide off the side of a pinnacle, and all you could tell of their whereabouts was the dust cloud they'd stir up. A few of the wildest went so far as to run theirselves down, get overheated with the big fat they was packing, and never cool off till they was stiff and dead.

There maybe was no rider to within a mile of 'em, but once they'd get kettled and stampede away they never knowed when to stop and they'd still be going at full speed when the death cold would overtake 'em and leave 'em flat to earth, never to run no more.

But the average of them cattle was mighty nice to handle; there was no slow poky riding when they was around, and if you knowed their ways everything was hunkydory; if you didn't you'd most likely find yourself doing a lot of wild riding without result only maybe wear your horse out. Some of the bunches we'd round up would be so wild that even while holding the herd on the cutting grounds, they'd keep on milling around and keep up a high lope. No man would ride inside of that herd unless he wanted 'em to just fly away like a bunch of quail. The cutting out was done from the outside of the herd, and when a steer was wanted out, the rider would just chip in on him, separating him from the rest of the herd before he knowed it.

He'd come out of the edge like a cannon ball, and the cowboy closest to him would sure have to do some tall riding to keep that steer from hitting for the hills instead of for the "cut" where he was wanted. There was times when the steer would get spooky and mad, and wouldn't turn even if you'd fan him acrost the face with your rope, sometimes that fanning would get him on the "prod" (fighting mad) and then them long horns of his would get mighty dangerous to both man and horse, but the *cowboy* never lets a critter get away, he'll take his rope down,

The first few that are cut out from the main herd for that "cut" sometimes couldn't be held in one spot, and they would have to be roped and tied down.

shake out a loop and dab it on around that six-foot spread of horns as the steer rushes in on him, misses (sometimes) and on past. The steer turns and makes another grand rush, and the cowboy will stay ahead out of his reach letting the slack of his rope drag on the ground. And when that same steer steps over the whale-line dragging along under him is when something happens, which sure upsets his plans of attack and everything in general.

The cowhorse'll pick up speed, the rope'll tighten up, and of a sudden that ornery critter will find his head brought up right alongside his hind quarters, lifted up in the air a few feet, only to be jerked down again, and not at all gently. The wind is knocked out of him sudden, and he's tied down with the "piggin string" before he can get it back.

The cowboy might leave him lay there to cool off for a spell and ride back to the herd, coiling up his rope on the way. When that steer is let up again he's most generally dubious about starting another fight and will most likely lope back to the cut kind of peaceable.

In starting a cut with them kind of cattle, the first few that are cut out from the main herd for that "cut" (as we call the bunch separated out) sometimes couldn't be held in one spot, and they would have to be roped and tied down; we'd keep on a-tying 'em down till there was enough there to keep the others we'd still be cutting out from getting too frisky or lonesome. Them what was tied down was a kind of an attraction for the others that was foot-loose and they'd stick around taking a sniff at the tied critters till there was enough of a herd cut out with 'em to keep 'em all company. After that, they was easy enough to hold till the herd was worked.

I'm sorry to say for the cowboy that there ain't no more of them cattle left, that is, not enough of 'em to speak of. The few you'll find are in the movies or following the rodeos, where the contestants ride and rope 'em both, then there might be a few more running loose on the range or up in the hills and turned wild again, but you might just as well say that they're gone, and gone for good.   For with the limit of the range there is nowadays there's got to be cattle on it that'll bring the most value per head, and I can't say that the longhorn was ever much of a beef producer, not comparing with the mixed Hereford and Durham stock you'll find on the range now.

And when I say I'm sorry for the cowboy that there's no more of the longhorn, it's that I know how much the cowboy liked to work them cattle.   I know how nice they was to stretch a new rope on, and how hard one of them steers would hit the other end, take all the kinks out of it and make 'er sing the whole forty-foot length.

Yessir, and them cattle was a lot of company too and always up to something. If they'd stampede they always done a good interesting job of it and make us ride for all we was worth and then some, and even when the nights was still and quiet they'd make you wish you could see through the dark so you could tell what they'd be up to then.

Like, for instance, the whole herd may be bedded down and resting contented like, two or three of us boys would be riding around 'em steady, keeping our distances apart and singing to 'em as we'd ride and all would seem hunkydory, but there was always a few of them natural born leaders in each herd, the kind that never sleeps much, and them would sure have to be watched

Amongst 'em would be a full-grown, long, and lanky steer with horns of the kind that could more than meet an argument with most anything.

mighty close. They'd wait till the riders made the round and was far enough away so they could make a sneak without being heard; then they'd ease out and step light till they was far enough and safe to break into a run and make their getaway.

But us boys was on night guard for the purpose of keeping 'em all together, and that we tried to do with the result that not many could ever sneak out without we caught up with 'em and turned 'em back in the herd.

You couldn't very well go to sleep on the job when them cattle was around, and whether it be on day herd, night guard, or on circle they had a way about 'em that sure kept a cowboy close to his saddle.   There was plenty of times when them critters would get over-ornery and when the cowboy would cuss 'em for a brainless animal, but there was things would happen every day while riding amongst 'em what would make the cowboy think again, and he'd wind up to admiring 'em and wondering how they could be so wise and in so many ways.

I remember how down in the border States where the water-holes are miles from the feed, the cattle would string out every two or three days and head for the troughs eight to twelve miles up into the foothills; there'd be a rocky trail most of the way over and too long for the little calves to make, so they'd be left behind.

Instinct, or maybe brains, made them little week-old fellers find a hiding spot before their mammies left for the day trip to water.   They'd cuddle up under any kind of brush where they'd be hid best and go to sleep till their mammies came back.   Many a time I've rode in on 'em when they was hiding that way, but they wouldn't move and you couldn't see 'em unless your horse near stepped on 'em.   If they did have to move they wasn't at all slow about it and for a distance would sure make themselves hard to catch; they'd travel along at full speed, make a circle, and if by that time you was gone would come right back, lay down, and hide at the exact spot where their mammy'd left 'em.

I've seen times when there'd be half a dozen or more of them little calves left behind that way and all hid along within a few feet of one another. One of them would maybe get out of his hiding place to stretch for a while, then up would come another one till they was all out and a-stretching, then of a sudden you'd hear a little beller out of one of 'em and tail up, kicking and

If a lone cow was making a losing fight trying to protect her calf, all
she had to do was let out a call and there'd be a herd
of big steers answering it.

a-bucking, he would race out acrost the flat, make his little circle, and come back. The rest of 'em would take up his lead and perform the same and play on that way till all the stiffness from the hiding position they'd been in was gone, when they'd hide again and wait for their mammies to relieve 'em.

But what always used to set me to thinking the most, was when I'd come across a bunch of them little fellers laying around anywheres, and not at all hid. The reason they wasn't hiding just then was a good one, for right amongst 'em would be a full-grown, long, and lanky steer with horns of the kind that could more than meet an argument with 'most anything.

That steer would stay on the job as guardian till the mothers trailed back. Along about sundown you could see 'em; picking up speed and walking faster and faster, they'd start bellering for their calves a mile away and the closer they'd get, the more they'd beller and the faster they'd walk, till they'd finally break into a trot, and tired as they'd be from that long trip, besides packing all the water they could hold, they'd manage to leave the "dry stuff" behind and get to their calves quick as they could.

The little fellers, hearing their mammies coming, begin to perk up their ears, then break out on a run to meet 'em, and even though to the human eye they may all look alike there's no confusion with the cow and her calf about which belongs to which. The nursing goes on and all seem plum satisfied with everything in general, the big steer finds himself all alone and, after watching the proceedings for a spell, seeing that all is O K, trails out by his lonesome, headed for the water-hole miles and miles away.

So there you be, while that critter had no use for the human and wasn't at all affectionate in any way, not mentioning how contrary and ornery she'd get or how sometimes she'd make you travel to keep out of her horns' way, there was occasions a-plenty when you'd find yourself a-cussing at 'er orneriness and at the same time admiring the wise way that critter did have of being ornery and keeping you a-guessing.

And what's to their credit is, if trouble come they'd meet that trouble together and fight it *together* to a finish. If a lone cow was making a losing fight trying to protect her calf, all she had to do was let out a call and there'd be a herd of big steers answering it; and whatever the enemy was, bears or wolves, they was put on the run and making far apart tracks. The human is the only enemy they had that would make 'em scatter and keep 'em a-dodging, and they took it out on him in ways that was ornery, sometimes even getting the best of him too.

PIÑON AND THE WILD ONES

CHAPTER VIII

YEARS ago, when horses wasn't worth keeping tab on and even their hide wouldn't bring a dollar, the range stuff — studs, mares, colts — ran most all unbranded. Broke stock was kept, but they wasn't worth much either, far as money was concerned. They strayed everywhere and picked their own range, winter or summer. Once in a while some Indian would catch a fresh horse to break for his own use. Outside of that, the range horses wasn't bothered much, if any. They got wild — wild as antelopes. What was left of the mustang strain that was running free was picked up again in the better-blooded wild horse and scattered from Sonora, Mexico, through the Buckskin Mountains in northern Arizona and up into the Nevada deserts.

There was a time when you could count them by hundreds, and it would seem as if the whole side of a mountain was moving, so covered was it with "broomtails" and so regular was they moving. Sometimes they'd get started by some rider and bunch up that way till there'd be four or five hundred in the herd. There are big valleys in the wild-horse countries — some a couple of hundred miles long and fifteen or so wide, going north and south, and flanked on both sides with steep, rough juniper and piñon-covered hills. These valleys used to be dotted with bunches of fuzztails, or wild horses.

Considered worthless at that time, they enjoyed their freedom for years until the migration of the farmer to the West started a demand for horses. In the East, too, a market sprang up, with the result that the boys around the cow camps started buying whale line. The rope was used in forty-foot lengths, with one end slipped through the fork of the saddle and tied fast to the horn, the other end swinging a twelve-foot loop.

The fuzztails was easy enough caught at first. They could be hazed into almost any kind of trap. But unless you were satisfied with some old mare or jug-headed yearling, you had to be mounted for roping a good one. Besides, roping was too slow. Generally you had to use relays of fresh horses and it was mighty hard on good saddle stock. Then the blind trap was brought into the game, and that's where Mister Wild Horse started using judgment. A trap was made either of cottonwood poles or of woven wire averaging eight feet high and fixed up with junipers to look as if it wasn't there. There was two corrals and wings stretching out sometimes a mile long on both sides of the main gate. It'd take a month or so for six of us to build such a trap, but when it was done it'd fool any human.

I remember that occasionally strangers going through the hills would get caught in our traps while following a trail and didn't know it till they were right up against the corral gate. I used often to think it'd be a humdinger of a place to run a horse thief into; he'd sure have to hoof it from there on, 'cause no horse could go through it.

The wild horses were thinning down in numbers and they were getting so they wouldn't run at every small scare. They began to save their legs and hoofs for a pinch. I remember when they would run thirty miles at just seeing some rider, not interested in ponies at all, passing through the valley. They got over running without reason and made sure that a rider was after them and meant business before they'd start. Even then they'd only keep a safe distance ahead; if the rider stopped or turned they'd gradually do the same and go on feeding.

They grew wiser right along to the ways of the human. They kept shy of the timbered hills where traps were known to be and grazed in the valleys where they could see ahead what they were running into in case running was necessary. We went to relaying on them on the flats and once in a while we'd get a bunch to work the way we wanted and head them into the hills. If we crowded them too much they'd split and go in all directions. We had to use our heads, 'cause the fuzztail sure used his. They had no rest in the valleys or mountains. They'd leave their home range to go to another only to get chased back.

Every cow-puncher with a string of his own ponies was soon running mustangs, cow-punching being too slow. Some were good at it and others only educated the mustang and made him harder to catch. A trap with a spring and a rope buried was invented for use on trails. When it was set off the rope'd fly up, circle a leg, and draw tight. The other end of the rope was fastened to a log. A trapped mustang would tear up the scenery a heap at first and then settle down to dragging that log far as he could, leaving a trail easily followed and seldom more than four miles or so in length. This sort of trap caught some horses, but generally they were old mares, the leaders of the bunch.

The fuzztail got wise to this snare and as there were cattle on the same range he'd use them as leaders. He'd follow the cattle as they started to water. If a trap caught anything, it was usually a steer that dragged the log. The leading horse would look back and nicker, seeing if her foals were all present and accounted for. And they would be.

Once while looking over the prospects for a new trap site, my outfit had stirred up a bunch of wild ones here and there to see which way they'd run. There must have been about three hundred head a few miles in front of us, covering the country at a stiff trot. We lagged behind and watched where they would naturally run without crowding.

More than two-thirds of them went through a big gap called Devil's Gate — a dandy natural place for a blind trap. We set to work there and the trap was up and strong in record time. Our saddle stock had a good rest and a steady feed of grain and they were rearing to go. The mere sight of a bunch of wild ones made them walk on two legs.

Meanwhile I'd been noticing a paint stud up on top of a big ridge at one side of the gap. He must have been a young one, 'cause there were only two fillies in his bunch. He had made his appearance a few times while we were building the trap and seemed to take a lot of interest watching us. I figured him to weigh close to eleven hundred. He was so good to look at that we decided to run him in first chance we got.

We were up long before daybreak the morning of the first run to our new trap. We'd had breakfast, our horses were caught and grain-fed, and we were riding out of camp by sun-up.

For two miles in depth, one right behind the other, come the wild ones.

It was fifteen miles to the trap and we planned to scatter from camp, hazing in wild ones on the way over. With another rider I headed on straight for the trap. We took our places close to the wings to help crowd the mustangs in and to keep them from leaving the trail before they got there — a ticklish job. We were off our horses and hidden behind a knoll, one man on each wing.

Somehow when I think of it now, I certainly feel sorry for the man that has never run mustangs. Anybody who likes excitement of the right kind sure would get it to his heart's content when looking back over the trail, winding around peaks on the mountain tops, while for two miles in depth, one right behind the other, come the wild ones, every one of them on the trail and every color of horseflesh you could think of! And all a-coming in, to order! I don't know how many heartbeats I lost or gained. And I was afraid those mustangs would hear the thumping under my shirt, for the leaders passed on the trail a few yards from where I was hid. The rest followed, sniffing for a suspicious sign; but we had taken good care that there would be none. The drags went past and I got on my horse, falling in behind. The boys caught up with us and before the mustangs knew it they was free no longer. That fence, which they couldn't see, was hard on them and skinned up quite a few, but they gradually quit hitting and started to milling. There was fifty-six head in the bunch, but scattered out as they was on the trail they seemed three times that many to anybody not used to the game.

About this time we saw the paint stud up on his ridge looking down at us. We'd get him next day, we agreed. But next day he wasn't to be seen in the neighborhood, nor the day after that. So we took our catch out of the trap by roping each one and tying one front foot to the tail close enough so he couldn't use it except to rest. They were fence-broken by this time and we took them to a big pasture furnished us by the outfit we were running for. The outfit owners wanted the range cleared of wild horses so that grazing for their cattle would be better. We was working under contract, the arrangement being that we take away all the horses caught except the branded ones. There was only one out of twenty bearing an iron and the rest we shipped or sold to buyers. It looks like easy money, but a lot of mustang-runners got disappointed in it and left the country with nothing but a few stove-up saddle horses.

The second drive to our promising trap looked better than the first. Being out on circle with three of the boys I could see that the wild ponies was coming in and taking to the trail fine. It wasn't just luck for us. It was because we'd been at it a lot and knew what we was about. We credited the mustang with brains and used ours against his. And ours won — sometimes.

The boys on the mountain flanks were riding in a steady lope with the fuzztails hitting it up half a mile or so ahead. All was working pretty and I'd already picked as a saddle horse a bald-faced, stocking-legged sorrel stud up in the lead bunch. They were as good as caught, for a quarter of a mile ahead was the wings. Then on that ridge at the right of the gap I see the familiar paint stud, appearing all excited. Head and tail up, he's coming down and heading for our bunch, snorting at every jump.

One of the boys at the wing tries to turn him back, but there wasn't a chance. That paint knows just where he's headed and what to do, and nothing but a trap fence could stop him. A loop

My saddle was jerked off my horse and I went sailing with it to Mother Earth.

spreads and reaches out, but it falls a couple of feet short. With a whistle and a snort the paint keeps on straight for the leaders that were behaving so well. As he nears them there's a sort of confab in horse language. And the paint takes the lead, seventy head of ponies following him! They broke out on their top speed, their tails a-popping; and down the mountain off the trail they went.

I'd figured something was going to bust when I saw the paint butting in that way and I headed my horse for the left flank of the herd. There was three of us trying to check the stampede and, even though we knew there was no use, we certainly rode and tried. We got there ahead of the paint, now running straight for us with the rest of the herd right in his dust. With our ropes over our heads we tried to faze them by yelling and whooping, but they kept coming and split on all sides of us. Two ropes sang out and settled over the paint's head with him going down-hill full speed. The whale-lines stretched out like a fence, tons of horseflesh hitting them, two pounds to the ounce. It was against our judgment, but we were mad. My saddle was jerked off my horse and I went sailing with it to Mother Earth, where I saw more horses' legs at one sitting, so to speak, than ever before in my life. The other rope broke and away goes the paint, bucking down the pinnacle and dragging my saddle and another piece of rope along with him. The horse I was riding joined the wild bunch, too, and when I calculated my losses I was short a new rope, a sixty-dollar saddle, a horse, and even my six-shooter, which had taken a squatter's right in some badger hole; anyhow, I couldn't find it. We had many reasons to get the paint now. He'd turn every bunch we'd bring. He knew where the trap was and he'd give us away every chance he got.

I rode to camp back of one of the boys and the next morning I made as a substitute saddle a relay rigging consisting of two stirrups, a strap, and a blanket. It took thirty-five pounds'

weight off my horse. We were all riding our tops that morning
and I knew if we got sight of Mister Paint he was a gone gosling.

From a summit we sighted out on the flat. I took first turn
and sashayed him for a good fifteen miles. Then one of the boys
relieved me and took him on. When I saw the paint again, the

I took first turn and sashayed him for a good fifteen miles.

fourth man was at him; he'd covered a good sixty miles in mighty
fast time. I could see he was going on his nerve, but he had
plenty of it. The fifth man jumped him, and after a quarter-
mile run on a fresh horse the paint was his. There was no trace
of my saddle with him; my rope must have broken at the hon-
doo. An unravelled piece of the other rope still hung to his
neck.

We sure took good care of that boy so he wouldn't get away.

We put him in the trap he'd watched us build, leaving him there overnight to think things over. In the morning we found him stretched out with a broken neck. He had hit the corral a little too hard.

Everything went well during the next circle we made till we got to that spot where the paint had spoiled things. It seemed as if there were a couple of fuzztails from the first bunch that remembered the turning point. Two of them took the lead away from our trap, at any rate, and we lost the bunch. It got us on edge to see such a promising trap site turn out so disappointing.

We ran two weeks and had caught forty head more when one day lightning struck and burnt a juniper down right in the main gate. That cooked our goose. You couldn't get a mustang within a mile of it.

Figuring on working both sides of it without having to turn a bunch, we gave our next trap two main gates. We caught some thirty-odd head in the first run. On the second day we lost all we brought in, the bunch turning within a few yards of the gate. The trouble was that a few doggone dudes from town had come up hunting sage chickens, which they cooked on a brush fire within a few steps of the trail. They must have been eating as they walked, for there were chicken bones chewed up and scattered all along. Their Number Ten shoe-prints were easily visible, and you couldn't push a mustang through there with a snow plough. We closed that gate and started running in from the other side. The jinx was on us there, again; a few head of stock had died a half mile up the draw above the trail

and a sniff was enough to turn off the suspicious mustangs, for
when they're being chased that way they are always suspicious.
Mustangs may even be superstitious; many a time I've seen
crows, flying over the leaders, squawk them off the trail. I've
had them turn on me for no reason that I could see. But that's
where they've got it on us humans; their instinct, sense of smell
and vision are developed to the hair-trigger point. It's plain
wild-horse sense.

We built two more traps and changed our tactics each time.
Even with our bad luck we caught more horses than anybody
else in that country. The boys I was with was professional
horse hunters — best hands at it I ever saw. And I was no
slouch myself or they wouldn't have had me with them. Our
main idea was to let the mustangs think they was getting away.
For instance, if we wanted them up on the mountain or wherever
our trap was, we'd make a bluff to run them in the opposite
direction and nine times out of ten they'd double back into the
trail to our trap.

We'd even build rag wings three or four miles long on each
side of the mountain to our trap by stringing a single wire on
far-apart posts with rags dangling from it. That would turn a
few, but sometimes some wise old mare in the lead would take
a chance and the others would follow through.

The popular idea of wild horses usually has some beautiful
stallion heading the band, but, although he may be beautiful,
the stallion seldom takes the lead. I've seen the old boy many a
time half a mile or so behind his bunch; he's there to see that his
mares, if chased, are getting away. He doesn't want to leave

any behind and will even nip some of the drags to make them run faster and keep up with the rest. Going to water or following a trail some old mare is always ahead with her foals following. The only time the stallion may take the lead is when the herd is in a pinch and crowded. But even then he'll circle around his mares, keeping them together and looking for the best way out at the same time. He'll find it if there is any. When two bunches meet, the stallion in each goes ahead by himself and has a little conversation with the other. The mares and colts wait and graze till the discussion is over and the stallion returns. Then the trail is resumed unless that talk winds up in a fight. Often it does — the winner taking all and the loser hits out alone. When the loser comes across another band it's another scrap, and if he wins, the bunch is his, whether they want him or not. Should some mare get ornery and want to leave, that stallion puts his head down, shoots his ears back, and, looking wicked, hazes her back to the herd.

We caught a lone stud once that had been whipped out of some bunch — caught him when he thought he was getting away from us. There were no other horses in the trap and he felt mighty spooky. A few of us was sitting on our horses at the main gate waiting till one of the boys went round and opened the little corral to drive him in. He'd been circling around testing the trap here and there and had found it mighty solid. He knew his only way out was the way he came in. He stopped and sized us up for a spell, fire in his eye. Then with ears back and teeth showing he made a bee line for one of the boys inside and off his horse. The man started to dodge out of the stud's

way but he went down. As Mister Stallion, heading for his
man, went past our line a loop sailed out and dropped over his
neck. He was drug down to the little corral and taken to the
pasture with the next bunch caught. A month later we found
him dead. It wasn't lockjaw or starvation that killed him.

The wild horse is always ready to go a long way, spring, summer,
fall, or winter.

He was fat as a seal and had plenty of feed and water. He just
died of a broken heart.

The wild horse I'm speaking of here is of the bunch-grass
countries, where he has a chance to develop and grow. His
brain is a heap keener than the desert horse's; he's bigger and
well proportioned, and on an average better built than any thor-

oughbred you ever saw. He's all action and steel, and if I had
my pick between a thousand-dollar Arabian steed and a common
fuzztail for my own use I'd rather have the one with the snort
and the buck, 'cause I know the trail between suns is never too
long for him, no matter how scarce the feed or water may be.

Plenty of times I've heard fellers talk of running down the
wild ones with grained horses in the spring of the year, when the
fuzztail is supposed to be weak. I've seen it tried and sometimes done, but I always figgered it a mighty hard proposition.
Fact is, I've seldom seen the fuzztails when they was weak —
not in that particular country anyhow; and unless a feller has a
lot of good saddle horses to run the legs off and an income that
keeps him from worrying about a living, I'd call it a mighty poor
way of going at it. The wild one is always ready to go a long
way, spring, summer, fall or winter; he can usually show you
where the trail ends, and you'll be by your lonesome when he
does it.

I remember a bunch of boys who had come up fresh from
Texas, all good hands at roping and riding and savvying stock.
They was drawing wages from the same outfit we was running
horses for, and I'd come up to their camp for a piece of beef. I
stuck around for a spell to hear news of the lower country and
while we was talking a bunch of mustangs came to water at the
creek just half a mile below camp. One of the boys sees them
and remarked: "How tame they are, coming to water that close
to camp."

"They ain't tame," I said. "They're just full of confidence
in themselves. Try your luck catching one of 'em."

No sooner said than done. The rider snared the fastest horse he could get and was up and at them with his rope dragging in less time than it takes to tell it. That part of the country, by the way, was full of junipers and piñons with deep washes and high ridges. The mustangs disappeared over the ridge and Tex was right in their dust.

In about an hour he came back, his rope all coiled up neat and where it belonged. He wasn't disappointed — it was just a new one on him and he wondered how it was done.

"Sure enough," he said, "the earth just swallowed 'em. I thought they was right in front of me and when I topped the ridge I couldn't see hair nor hide of 'em. I circled and looked for tracks, but that whole country is already full of horse tracks."

Texas holds the record for good cow hands, but cow-punching and mustang-running are a heap different. I suppose this particular bunch of mustangs strung themselves out straight ahead till they got out of sight in the thick brush and then just doubled back close to their own trail. Of course Tex just kept going, and by the time he circled, the fuzztails were out of the country.

Before leaving we built two more traps on that range, with pretty fair results. All together we had caught, shipped, and sold more than five hundred head. With winter coming we decided to pull out for the south and run some more when the snow wasn't so deep.

The superintendent of the outfit rode up to our camp the day before we left and said his instructions from the owners was to kill off the rest of the mustangs, two dollars a head being offered as bounty. Of course the owners didn't know anything about running stock, but they realized from what the superintendent said that something would have to be done to save the range for the cattle. The owners was probably leading a soft life back East busy with their social functions and taking shower baths in champagne regular. I guess they didn't realize or care what they were condemning to die just so there could be more room for the cattle and a bigger income for themselves.

Naturally, we refused flat, saying that if we didn't want to, or couldn't, catch the mustangs, we sure wouldn't shoot them. And we left.

By the time we got to our next mustang territory our saddle stock was leg-weary, and after sizing up the country we decided to postpone any more running till along about spring. In the meantime we took possession of a deserted mining camp and made ourselves at home for the winter. We kept graining our horses and with the bunch grass in the hills they grew fat. Some of the boys made McCarthies, or hair ropes, while others worked with the steel traps. Pretty soon we had a good-sized bale of furs to ship — coyotes, bobcats, badgers, and one cougar that was shot. We kept down expenses, and managed to be present at all dances within sixty miles of our camp.

Towards spring we built three water traps — just a corral in plain sight built around a water hole with a smaller corral connected in which to keep what was caught, and by that keeping the main corral for another bunch. There was two main gates, one on each side, and they was left open, as we wasn't figgering on catching any mustangs just then. As water got scarce, later on — water holes being some forty miles apart — the mustangs gradually came up closer to our traps every night.   Finally, one night I saw the tracks of some that had been right inside the trap to drink.   They got used to it and they'd come in one gate, drink what they wanted, rub themselves for a spell, and leave through the other gate.   In time there was from four to six bunches watering at each trap.

We kept away and let the mustangs run back and forth through our traps for over a month.   We'd ride the whole country and at each water hole where there was no traps a man would be there to keep the wild ones from drinking.   Then they'd begin to trail out for the springs we had corralled.

A day came when the flats of the desert went dry as a bone. It was our time to work.   We split in pairs, two men to each trap, closed one gate and left the other open.   Near the traps we had dug holes big enough for a man to get into comfortable, covering them over with poles, dirt and brush.   We'd take shifts of half a night — the wild horse waters at night mostly — watching from these holes.   One man slept while the other watched. I had second guard the first night and missed the fun, but the first man on guard pulled the trigger rope and caught twelve head.   Counting the catches in the other traps we got twenty-seven of the wild ones that night.

The next night I had better luck.   While I was in the hole familiar snorts told me that a bunch was coming.   I could tell they was suspicious of man scent even though I was quite a distance from the gate.   They'd come up a few steps, then go back; the lead mare would start ahead and the stud would circle around, his head up and taking in all he could see.   At times he'd turn the lead mare back, but he wasn't sure. The bunch was in need of water bad. Finally, half of them went in, only to come out again, snorting at every jump and shying at nothing. I knew they'd come back, and they did after a good hour's wait. I was wondering if I could catch the whole bunch, but when they came again they seemed to get reckless and crowded in and around the water. While the stud was acting nervous around his bunch I pulled the trigger and the gate closed with a bang. The bunch stampeded at the noise and struck out for the other side of the corral, the earth shook. As they hit the wire it yielded a little and kicked them back off their feet. Those mustangs tested the whole corral — every inch of it — but it was built for that purpose. Heavy wire cables had been stretched around the top and bottom of each post, making the whole corral as if it was one piece; woven wire was attached to the cable top and bottom and wired to the posts, being allowed to hang slack for give and take. I kept away from the trap after I'd made my catch, 'cause my appearance there just then would have made the horses break their necks hitting the other side.

The southern ponies were not nearly so big or so well built as the northern horses we'd been running, and they was caught more easy, 'cause they hadn't been chased so much. Blind traps was unknown in that country. An open corral with long wings or a water trap was the average. Southern mustangs was easy turned and handled, and on a fast horse you could often ride close enough to one to pile your rope on him. They was generally caught around water holes, 'cause when full of water the mustang can't run very fast or far.   But in that shape, he's easy choked if the rider don't ease up on the rope in time.

Our traps began to wear out after a while, and the mustangs, still running loose, learned to keep shy of the closed water holes. There was no escaped fuzztail to give us away, but the bunches was leaving the country and hitting for new range.   We opened all the gates again and left the traps for a couple of months.   A few bands of wild ones came back and started watering, but when we closed the gate on the other side, leaving only the trap gate open, they got suspicious.   Their snorts was all that was necessary to let us understand that they knew the corral was ready for business, and in a long lope they hit back to the country from which they came.

Once we caught a black stud that had been caught before and was already acquainted with the nature and strength of a trap.   Ours being new to him and well hid, he was fooled just long enough to be caught again but he didn't waste time hitting the sides of the trap as the rest of the bunch with him did.   He figgered just how high that trap was and used the speed he was coming in with to clear it!   He never checked up or stopped. He sailed right on over the top and never touched the cable. The fence at that particular place was nine feet high.   A mustang seldom jumps anything; he tries to go through first. But this one had learned there was no going through.   I never saw anything so pretty as when that black horse got clean away. Our mouths was wide open, and we stared.   It was a well-done job too; for instead of breaking into a run after clearing the fence he just trotted off stiff-legged, covering fifteen feet to the pace.

His feet seemed not to touch the ground, his muscle working and his head up, he looked back at us over his shoulder and fanned his long tail about just as if he was waving by-by to us. He stopped sudden on top a little hill three hundred yards or so from us, and facing about he gave us a farewell whistle before proceeding, full of pride, out of sight. Pete looked at me solemn and said: "My God, Bill, I'd give a good hundred for that horse!"

The hardest horse to trap is the one that has been broke to riding or work and then gets away. No matter how gentle he was when he got away, the sight of his home range and the wild ones makes him forget all that man has ever taught him. The only thing he remembers and uses is his knowledge of the ways of man. This knowledge stands him in good stead when he sees some rider fogging down on him; that wise hombre takes the lead and the bunch follows, sure that they've got a leader that knows the ropes.

I've known of mustangs' getting away after being gentled that travelled two hundred miles or more, through settlements, over bridges and railroad tracks, even swimming rivers to their country of freedom. They'd feed as they travelled, not even stopping to drink; they'd go up or down a stream, dragging their noses in the water till their thirst was satisfied. If you could catch up to them before getting close to their home territory they wasn't so hard to handle; being in a strange country, they'd give up easy enough. The mustang has a good working set of brains; if he sees, for instance, that whoever is chasing him is riding a tired horse he knows it and will circle round, tail and head up, looking pretty and teasing the rider to come on.

Talking of horse sense, let me bring in a chestnut I'd picked on as a saddle horse. He needed some care for the cuts and scratches he'd got when connecting with the trap. I roped and snubbed him, put on the hackamore, and picketed him to a log in a little meadow close to the corral. He had fifty feet of soft rope to run on and the feed was good, but the flies and mosquitoes was hard on him, the deer fly and the bulldog fly doing the most tormenting; and that poor little chestnut had a lot of places open for the pests to work on. I wanted to heal up the sores before thinking of breaking him, and his badly peeled head gave me a lead to show my feelings.

The first time he saw me coming I'd thought he'd leave the country until the heavy log caught in a stump; then he bit and kicked at the picket rope. I let him have it out and kept coming closer, working round till I touched his head. He'd run his nose up along my arm, then snap at it and strike with both front feet at the same time. I worked pretty easy, 'cause I didn't want him to lose any more of that hide, and he only showed the right spirit according to his lights, even if he did come within close striking distance of my face. I could have taken advantage of him and ridden him while he was sore, when he would have been easier to break maybe, but I had a lot of time and I liked him. Before long I had his peeled head all covered with fly-proof healing salve; I smeared a lot of that salve on all the sore spots from the tip of his nose to the middle of his back. I'd do that twice and three times a day till finally he got to looking for me and nickered when he saw me coming. He'd come to meet me as far as the picket rope would let him and follow me around wherever I went. I kept smearing salve on all the cuts plumb down to his hoofs and he'd stand there just watching me, not a bit of harm in him. He was healing up fast and hair began to cover the scars. One day I even got on him bareback and rode him around the log. He took that all in as part of the healing process, I guess. Anyhow, he got over being afraid of me.

He was the kind of sensitive horse that wouldn't stand rough handling, and his ten hundred pounds of fine bone and muscle could back his sentiments in that regard. He was full of fight and only a little jerking around was needed to start him going. I didn't jerk him but kept on handling him easy, until one day I slipped my saddle on him. He did just what I expected, giving the prettiest exhibition of bucking I ever saw. I was wondering how hard a ride I'd have to put up to stick him when I saddled him again a few days later, but he fooled me. I led him round a bit; he stood quiet till I got my seat. I pulled him on one rein a couple of times and finally lined him round the corral. He just trotted on and kept looking back at me. I was expecting him to go to pieces at any minute, but nothing doing. He acted as if everything was O. K. so long as I was up there sitting on him, and after smelling the saddle a few times he figgered that that must be all right too.

That summer and fall the chestnut and I had a lot of dealings together. I was headed for no place in particular — just drifting. I had a pack horse along and on top of him was my home and grub. We'd travel for a spell and take it easy when we'd strike places where the feed was good. We was out of

the wild-horse country when I quit putting hobbles on the chestnut and we was getting pretty thick by that time. Piñon, as
I called him, wouldn't go more than a few hundred yards from
my camp, no matter how scarce the feed was; and many a time
I would wake up at night to find that he and the pack horse was
bedded down right in the kitchen, you might say — just a rope's
length from my bed.

Piñon was no sugar-eater or pet. He was just a fifty-fifty
partner of mine. He never had a feed of grain, but once in a
while I'd give him a biscuit from my small Dutch oven. He'd
pack me all day long, but when I decided to camp I'd always
tend to Piñon and the other horse before straightening out my
camp or cooking a meal. If on a real hot day I'd come across a
juniper in the foothills, I'd always stop in what shade there was
under it and loosen up my saddle to air Piñon's back and scratch
him behind the ear every once in a while.

One day I had to stop in a town to get some grub and to-
bacco. I left Piñon and the other pony at the stable corrals.
Seeing that the big mangers was full of hay, I sneaked out when
I thought Piñon wasn't looking. But he soon found out that I
was missing and the little son-of-a-gun was sure making himself
heard! Well, sir, I wouldn't have taken the whole world for
that little horse just then, or I guess any other time, either. I
finally told the stable boy to watch out that Piñon didn't hurt
himself on the fence and started out toward the main street of
town, walking a heap faster than I generally do. I got my stuff
and came back as quickly as I could, to find a mighty restless
pony waiting for me. I saw that I would simply have to camp

with him that night, so I picked out a clean spot in an out-of-
the-way corner of the corral to roll out my bed. Piñon was
right there to see what was up; and as soon as he discovered I
was making my camp, as he'd seen me do many times before, he
was satisfied and walked away to eat. I figgered having lost his
freedom and being in a strange country he looked to me as a sort
of leader and partner; I felt that he was a little orphan and kind
of needed me.

This isn't intended to be a lot of sentimental talk I'm handing you. Piñon might have been the exceptional horse in a
thousand, but I find that if you make a pal of any gelding and
talk to him often, treating him about as you would a dog, you'll
have a stouter friend in the horse. A dog may go mad, turn
on you, and chew you up if grub's scarce and he gets hungry
enough; but the horse will pack you as far as he can and die
doing it. If you're out on the desert and you both give out he
won't howl his sufferings into your ear. As for brains and
honesty — I hate to compare a dog or any other animal with
the deep-hearted, long-winded pony of the Western ranges.

For years Piñon and I roamed the hills, valleys, and deserts,
and gradually the time came when if I went away he wouldn't
fret so much; he knew I'd surely come back, and I always did.

When the war broke out and I joined in I felt as if I had
some one dependent on me; but then men was leaving their
mothers, wives, and children behind. Before taking off my boots,
chaps, and spurs for the uniform I saddled old Piñon and headed
for a country where I knew the mustangs was free from runners
and where the range was good. I was leading an extra horse

to ride back. When in a few days I rode up on the pass where Piñon was to get his freedom once more I could see here and there down in the valley a few bunches of wild ones, and a couple of miles down the ridge I could make out four head feeding. A bunch so small generally is young studs kicked out of a herd by an older stallion. I knew this bunch would let Piñon come in and run with them, so I headed down in the wash and out of sight.

I'm facing the breeze now, making it possible for me to come pretty close without the wild ones getting wind of me. Within fifty yards of them, with a small ridge between us, I slip off the chestnut and sneak through the buckbush to get a peek at what sort of ponies they are. I see marks on their backs showing that they was once saddle horses, turned wild again, and wiser than ever. A better bunch to turn old Piñon with I couldn't hope for; I am sure these can never be caught — not with Piñon in the lead, anyway.

Unsaddling quick as I can, and acting as if I'm going to camp, I lead Piñon to a place where he can get sight of the other horses. Then giving him a couple of farewell pats I drop back a little. He sees the bunch and walks up to investigate. I'm down flat on the ground, but I can tell what's going on by watching my little horse; he gets acquainted, but pretty soon, as I figgered, he comes back. I lead him up again and pat him once more, and gradually, looking back at me now and again, he works over the ridge out of sight. I'm in the wash where my other horse is tied and, grabbing my chance, ride back for the summit fast as I can make it, being sure to keep out of sight while getting there. On reaching the summit I look back; one horse is apart from the others, rummaging around where I was going to camp. "Great little horse!" I say to myself, and it's all I can do to keep from going back for him. Then again I figure he's a heap better off where he is. As I watch, Piñon tops the little ridge between him and the other horses. He went to them, knowing that some day I'd come back for him.

I did come back, of course, but it was several years later. When I topped that summit once more, how good that little country, hid away from civilization, looked to me after seeing what I did of war and the suffering world! I camped in the wash close to the ridge where Piñon and I parted. Early the next morning I was up and riding the hills and valleys for a sight of him. At first I had no hopes much, but when the sun had only two hours to go in the west I saw five head a couple of miles away following the trail out of sight over a hill. I had a hunch, and, taking my chance to catch up with them, I follows.

They was on a little flat and there was no way I could come closer without being seen, so without trying to hide I tied my horse to a juniper and walked out towards them.

Piñon is in the lead, feeding. He sees me and with a snort warns the others. I talk to him just as I used to, but he's too far away, maybe, to hear me. In a big cloud of dust they're gone, but only to circle, Piñon leading them back to a safe three hundred yards from me. There he stops, tosses his head up and down, and smells the air and the ground. He's forgot me. The many days of sunlight, snow, and freedom since he saw me last have been long enough to heal many a scar and make him forget a friend. I try to get a little closer, talking away so Piñon will maybe remember. Now it almost seems that he does — he comes up a few steps as if to meet me as he used to. The other horses, doubtful of his actions, turn and start to run, which leaves Piñon alone and undecided what to do. But soon enough the wild blood wins and, with a shake of his head and his long mane to the wind, he breaks out on the easy lope I know so well, headed for the wild bunch and the freedom I had once taken away from him.

I'm always mighty proud of that little horse and I like to think of him often. There are quite a few like him in the wild-horse countries and I'm kind of sorry now so many was caught, 'cause I have a lot of respect and admiration for the mustang. The fact that he'd give us back the same medicine we'd hand him, with sometimes a little overdose, only made me feel that in him I had an opponent worthy of the game. Even though I'd get sore at them when they'd put it over on us and rub it in a little too hard, the satisfaction I'd get at catching some wise bunch didn't last very long when I'd remember that they'd be shipped, put to work, and maybe starved into being good by some hombre who was afraid of them and didn't savvy at all. For they really belong, not to man, but to that country of junipers and sage, of deep arroyos, mesas — and freedom.

S Clara C-10

This book is

P9-EDI-007

CRISSY AT THE WHEEL

By the Same Author

PEACHTREE ISLAND

SAND IN HER SHOES

THE HOMEMADE YEAR

TALLIE

Crissy AT THE WHEEL

BY MILDRED LAWRENCE

Illustrations by Marvin Bileck

HA EW YORK

This book is from the:
santa clara
county
library district

SANTA CLARA COUNTY LIBRARY

3 3305 00796 1810

COPYRIGHT, 1952, BY

HARCOURT, BRACE AND COMPANY, INC.

All rights reserved, including the right to reproduce
this book or portions thereof in any form.

first edition

LIBRARY OF CONGRESS CATALOG CARD NUMBER: 52-6904

PRINTED IN THE UNITED STATES OF AMERICA

In this book, I am much indebted to memories of my old home, Flint, Michigan, from whose history I have adapted many scenes, several events, and, I hope, the pioneering spirit which has carried Flint successfully through its three great eras—lumbering, carriage-making, and automobile manufacturing. My thanks are due also to the many individuals—both strangers and friends—who have, by personal interviews or by their written reminiscences, provided me with a picture of a typical carriage-making town just after the turn of the century. The characters are of course entirely fictional.

Mildred Lawrence

Orlando, Florida

This book is from the:
santa clara county
library district

Contents

CRISSY AT THE WHEEL

1

NO MATTER WHAT
THE HORSES SAY

Crissy came to the head of the stairs and peered cautiously
over the rail. Aunt Henrietta was nowhere in sight and
there was a buzz of polite voices from the parlor, where
the ladies of the Granite City Diamond Jubilee Committee
were already making plans for the big celebration next
summer.

"The banisters look dusted," Crissy told Susan-Cat, who
was rubbing energetically against her black-stockinged legs,

This book is from the:

santa clara
county
library district

"so I think we'll just take a chance."

She scooped Susan-Cat up under one arm, seated herself sidesaddle on the banister and went flying down. Susan-Cat looked rather matronly and not at all the type to enjoy sliding down banisters, but Crissy knew better. Susan always purred the loudest when she was going somewhere very fast. Crissy landed with a slight thump, because she was going to meet Papa at the train and so had her shoes on for a change.

"Might as well get used to it, anyway," she told Susan-Cat, "with school starting next week."

"Clarissa Jane, is that you?" Aunt Henrietta called from the parlor.

"Yes'm."

Crissy twisted around to make sure that she had not mussed her starchy white dress. There just might be a small streak of dust on the back of one long ribbed stocking, but that was certainly Aunt Henrietta's fault for not cleaning better.

"You aren't sliding on the banisters, are you?" asked Aunt Henrietta.

"No, ma'am," said Crissy glibly. "I'm standing right here in the hall."

That, of course, was the absolute truth. It was just lucky that Aunt Henrietta hadn't spoken a minute sooner. Crissy didn't see, anyway, why Aunt Henrietta was so set against her sliding down banisters. It had something to do with being a lady, even at eleven years old, and was all wound up with shoes being better than bare feet, and curls being better than fat black braids, and Martha May Garrett being a better companion than Elmo Hawkins, who was much more interesting but was a boy and therefore not a suitable playmate.

Aunt Henrietta pushed aside the green velvet portieres and swished out into the hall.

"You could have come down sooner and spoken to the ladies," she said. "Over at the Garretts' the other day, Martha May was so polite— But there, I have to get back to the committee meeting. It's dragging on and on, so you'll have to go after your father yourself. Peg's all hitched up."

Crissy tried not to look too much delighted. She loved to drive Peg, who used to be a race horse, but mostly Aunt Henrietta drove, to make sure Peg didn't go too fast.

Crissy and Papa liked to play race track when Aunt Henrietta was not along. They could play it any time, of course, but Aunt Henrietta hated to have her hair blown and, as Papa said, Aunt Henrietta had given up a lot to come and keep house for him and Crissy since Mama died.

"Maybe I ought to start right now," said Crissy hopefully. "The train might be early."

"Go along, then," said Aunt Henrietta. "Don't go too fast, and watch out for the corner downtown. You can get out and lead Peg if you're afraid." She gave Crissy's skirt a little twitch. "You look very nice and neat."

That was real praise from Aunt Henrietta, but Crissy could always feel her aunt's disappointment that Crissy was not more like Martha May, who had floating golden curls and looked like a pearly angel in ruffly white dresses with pale blue sashes. About all Crissy could ever manage was to be neat, because her black hair was as straight as a stick, she had mostly sharp corners instead of curves, and her complexion was so tanned that she couldn't look like an angel no matter what she wore.

"Oh, well," Crissy told Susan-Cat, "we can't all be pretty, and I do have a lot of fun talking to the wrong people."

As she scrambled into the surrey and clucked to Peg, she hoped that she would meet some of the wrong people on the way to the station. If she went just a little out of the way, she might see Jed Haley, the striper down at the Carriage Works. And she wouldn't have to go out of the way at all to talk to Elmo, who lived just around the corner and raised rabbits in the back yard.

And of course at the depot there would be Papa, who was the best person of all, even though Aunt Henrietta did think he talked too much to Crissy about such unfeminine subjects as horse racing and, worse, that noisy novelty, the horseless carriage.

"Now, Hen, we Binghams make our living out of horses —indirectly, that is," Papa would say while Crissy shivered deliciously. She wished that she could call her dignified aunt "Aunt Hen," but of course nobody but Papa would dare. "And we might make our living out of horseless carriages before we get through, too."

"Oh, Andrew, don't be so silly," Aunt Henrietta always said uneasily. "Nobody is ever going to take those dreadful things seriously."

Papa and Crissy knew better than that, though. Why, in 1901, just last year, a young man named Roy Chapin had driven a horseless carriage from Detroit to New York in only a week. Papa said that some day— But Crissy guessed she would wait until she got to the station, because it was ever so much more fun to hear Papa say things than just to think about them herself. He would have an extra lot of things to say this time, because he had been clear to New York City to a carriage dealers' convention.

Crissy urged Peg into a trot, even though she knew she would have to stop in just a minute in front of Elmo's house. She did like to arrive with a flourish, so Elmo would forget for a minute that she was only a girl. Elmo was stalking up and down the front walk, wheeling his baby sister in her go-cart and looking over his shoulder to make sure nobody was going to catch him at it.

"You having company?" asked Crissy when she saw that the baby had on her best crocheted bonnet and that Elmo, like Crissy, was wearing shoes and stockings and was scrubbed until every freckle stood out as though it had been painted on.

"Naw!" Elmo looked disgusted. "Going to the Garretts' for supper, and Mama says I have to be a little gentleman. Hey, don't you want to wheel the baby?"

Crissy shook her head. She did wheel the baby for Elmo sometimes, usually in return for being allowed to go fishing with him down at the Branch, but not today.

"I'm going to the depot to get Papa," she announced proudly.

"Don't you even want to see the rabbits?" asked Elmo, not giving up hope. "I got ten new ones."

Crissy shook her head again, this time a little more slowly. She did love the baby rabbits, so tiny and furry, but it would be terrible if she were late for the train.

"I have to go," she said wistfully. "You going fishing tomorrow?"

"I might. By myself." Elmo stared at her tantalizingly and chanted in a hideous singsong,

> "Clarissa Jane Bingham
> Always wears gingham."

Crissy, who hated to be called by her whole name, let it pass for the moment. Elmo didn't know yet that she had found out what his middle name was by listening from the cherry tree while Aunt Henrietta talked to Elmo's mother. It would be fun, she thought, to start calling him Elmo Fauntleroy Hawkins, but she would rather wait for a better occasion.

"I didn't want to go, anyway," she said loftily. "Seeing Papa's going to be home, he might take me down to the Carriage Works."

She started Peg off again and left Elmo looking after her with what she hoped was envy.

"Oh!"

She gave a little jump, because Susan-Cat suddenly leaped over from the back seat and planted herself on Crissy's lap.

"Anyway, Papa'll be glad," she decided.

Papa liked Susan-Cat, no matter where she was, but Aunt Henrietta thought that Susan should not go riding in the surrey because she left white hairs on the broadcloth upholstery and on the velvet carpeting.

"If you must buy the most expensive surrey in the catalog, you might at least keep that cat away from it," Aunt Henrietta scolded. "Velvet carpets and oil lamps! I should think the Standard would have suited us fine, and you with a child to raise!"

Crissy didn't see what raising a child had to do with surreys, but she was glad that Papa drove the Jumbo instead of the Standard, which had plain carpet on the floor and no lamps at all.

"A salesman has to drive his best product," Papa always said placidly. "Makes the buyer want one, too."

Crissy settled Susan-Cat more comfortably and maneuvered Peg through the new arches of electric lights that spanned River Street at thirteen different places and made it look like a starry fairyland at night. Crissy sniffed a little at the idea of Aunt Henrietta thinking she might be afraid to drive Peg downtown. All the same, she was so busy watching out for farmers' wagons and road carts that she was almost afraid to glance at the Carriage Works. It was worth the risk, though, to catch a glimpse of Jed Haley, painting hairline stripes on the hubs and spokes of the shining new carriages.

As usual, Jed saw her through the wide double door of the paint shop, which was standing open. He swept off the derby hat which he wore all day and, some people said, all night, too, removed the fat cigar which was also his constant companion, and bowed just as though Crissy were a grown-up lady.

" 'O mistress mine, where are you roaming?' " he shouted, so that several old men lounging against the building stared curiously at Crissy. "(William Shakespeare, born 1564, died 1616.)"

"I'm going to the depot to get Papa!" Crissy shouted back, knowing that Aunt Henrietta would have considered a polite bow much more correct.

Aunt Henrietta thought that Jed Haley was not a proper person for her to know, but that, of course, was because of the cigar and the derby hat and because Jed talked more like a book than he did like real people.

"I can understand him perfectly," Crissy always protested. "He's very interesting. I don't know anybody else who can speak pure Shakespeare."

Aunt Henrietta hated to object to anybody who knew as much about literature as Jed Haley did, but she did murmur something about his fingernails being dirty.

"That's mostly red paint," said Crissy, "or sometimes yellow. It won't come off—not with turpentine or anything. My goodness, all stripers have paint on them!"

Susan-Cat uncurled from Crissy's lap, sat herself regally on the seat alongside, and looked out expectantly.

"You know when we come to the racing place, don't you?" Crissy asked.

Ahead of her lay the south end of River Street, lined with big houses set far back from the avenue. Here there was a long, straight stretch before the street swept up the hill to the depot.

"We could certainly go a little faster here," said Crissy, "seeing there's nobody in sight."

Peg pricked up her ears and went into a smart trot. Crissy's braids flew out behind her, Susan's whiskers blew in the breeze, and Peg went faster and faster. Crissy grinned. This was the way she loved to go, flying over the ground just the way a bird must fly through the air. Papa said that he wouldn't be surprised to see people really flying through the air like birds some day, but Crissy guessed likely he was just making believe, the way he did sometimes.

Crissy slapped the reins against Peg's back, and Peg rolled a questioning eye toward her.

"All right, Peg. You can go faster than that," urged Crissy, yielding happily to temptation.

This time Peg really picked up her feet and went. The wheels of the surrey hummed, the wind whistled past Crissy's ears, and the landscape rolled by in a dizzying blur.

"It's lovely!" sighed Crissy. "Just lovely! I do wish— Oh!"

Peg and the surrey swooped around a curve, barely missing another rig coming from the other direction. Crissy caught a horrified glimpse of Mrs. Garrett, dignified in stiff sailor hat and high-necked shirtwaist, and Martha May, with every curl in place, proceeding at a staid gait toward home.

"Whoa, Peg!" cried Crissy as soon as the Garretts were safely out of sight around the curve. "Oh, dear, Mrs. Garrett's sure to tell Aunt Henrietta!"

Of course there was always a chance that Mrs. Garrett would be too busy helping the hired girl fix supper for Elmo's folks to remember about Crissy, but it wasn't very likely. Mostly Mrs. Garrett remembered things very well, especially things that Crissy wished she wouldn't.

Crissy pulled to the side of the road, wound the reins around the whipsocket, and tried to smooth her ruffled hair. Papa wouldn't care, of course, but there might be somebody else at the depot who would notice that Crissy Bingham came to meet her father looking as though she hadn't combed her hair for a week. By the time she felt more smoothed out, she heard the whistle of the train and had to hurry after all to get to the depot in time.

"You stay here," she told Susan-Cat when Peg was safely tied to the hitching post beside the depot platform. "I'll be back pretty soon."

She did love to meet trains, especially when Aunt Henrietta wasn't there to keep her from running beside the coach where she had spied Papa's lean, brown face. Some specks of coal soot smeared her white dress, but she didn't suppose she could be blamed for that. All that mattered was getting to Papa as soon as possible, and in just a min-

ute he was there, swinging himself down from the high step and grinning fondly at Crissy.

"Oh, Papa!"

Crissy threw her arms around his neck and let him lift her off the ground for an exciting minute.

"Mmp!" Papa pretended to groan at the weight. "My, my, you must have been eating nothing but paving stones since I left!" He pushed his stiff straw hat back on his head and mopped his face. "Red plush and cinders are warm this time of year. Where's Hen? Too hot for her to get out of the surrey?"

"She couldn't leave on account of the Jubilee meeting, so she let me come by myself," said Crissy proudly. "Susan-Cat's here, too."

"Fine!" Papa picked up his battered leather valise and

headed toward the surrey. "How about a little horse racing on the way home? Does the track look fast?"

"Oh, yes!" cried Crissy. "Very fast. I mean— Well, I raced some on the way. Mrs. Garrett saw me."

"Very likely. Mrs. Garrett sees most things. Move over, Susan. You think you're going to drive this rig?"

Susan purred and moved over amiably so that she was wedged between Crissy and Papa. Peg backed expertly, and in a minute they were all flying down River Street, even faster than Crissy had dared to go.

"Bleep! Bleep!"

The big red Panhard automobile which belonged to Mr. Hanover, the richest man in town, swept by them with a roar. Peg reared, and two ladies, with their chiffon veils swirling behind them, turned to stare from the rear seat.

"Oh!"

Crissy gazed blissfully after them. The only other time she had seen the Panhard, which Mr. Hanover had imported from France, it had been standing still in front of the bank, being stared at by half the town. It was twice as exciting to see it flashing by, with the horn blowing and the passengers chattering gaily, exactly like a picture Crissy had seen in a fashionable magazine—fascinating and almost unbelievable.

Peg tried valiantly to keep up, but the Panhard vanished down the road in a cloud of dust. They were almost down-

town before Papa said, "Better give it up, girl," and slowed
Peg almost to a walk.

"That's the way I'd like to go," said Crissy, breathless
from her own ride and from the sight of the incredible
Panhard. "Fast, faster, fastest."

"You should have been with me in New York," said
Papa. "I saw horseless carriages that went even faster than
that. I even rode in some."

"Some?" cried Crissy. "You mean they have a lot there?"

"Dozens," said Papa. "Hundreds, for all I know. Crissy,
they make carriages look like nothing at all." He grinned
a little. "When they run, that is." His face grew sober
again. "I tell you there are big things coming, Crissy—big
changes in all our lives."

Crissy sighed and leaned back in the seat. This was the
kind of talk she loved, all about what was going to happen
any year now. As Papa talked, she could almost see all the
horses and wagons vanishing from River Street, while
horseless carriages roared gaily up and down, carrying not
only people but also fresh vegetables and packages from
the stores, and driven, Papa said, even by ladies.

"But you must call them automobiles now," Papa said.
"Everybody in New York does, and the *Scientific American*
does, too, in all their articles. Whoa, now, Peg! Steady,
girl!"

Peg sidestepped nervously across the street, even though

Dr. Agnew's horseless carriage—automobile, Crissy corrected herself hastily—was sitting perfectly still beside the
road, neither smoking nor roaring, as it usually did. Dr.
Agnew had had it built at the blacksmith shop from his
own design, and sometimes it ran but mostly it didn't.

"Should we stop and ask?" Crissy wondered.

She was always doubtful about saying much to Dr.
Agnew ever since Martha May had told her that Aunt Henrietta had been engaged to him once on a time and had
broken it off for some reason. Crissy thought Dr. J. Chauncey Agnew was very impressive—tall and elegant, with a
neatly clipped mustache—but not the kind of a doctor
people would call Doc, the way people did old Dr. Miles.

Papa handed the reins to Crissy and walked over to the
doctor, who glared at his machine and gave the crank at
the side an angry whirl.

"Afternoon, Chauncey," said Papa. "What do you think
of the future of the horseless carriage?"

The motor roared briefly and was silent again. Dr. Agnew
muttered something under his breath. Papa tried the crank
himself while Crissy gazed in fascination. Seeing both the
automobiles of Granite City in one day was almost more
excitement than she could bear. There was a clanking sound
from Dr. Agnew's machine, and a small puff of black smoke
floated into the air and disappeared.

"Cassius!" roared the doctor. "Where are you?"

Cassius, Dr. Agnew's colored boy, who had been standing as usual at the head of Rex, the doctor's big black horse, brought the rig up beside the stalled automobile.

Cassius always drove Rex and the doctor's old carriage behind the automobile, because at least half the time the doctor had to transfer himself and his little black bag to the carriage in order to get to his calls. Crissy didn't know how many times she had seen Dr. Agnew's automobile being towed home by a team of stout farm horses. She thought, anyway, that it looked more natural behind a horse, because, except for the tiller to steer by and the flywheel showing underneath, the machine looked exactly like any other carriage on the road. Most automobiles did, Papa had explained, except the French ones or some of the more expensive American models with special bodies.

"Anybody who can make this diabolical machine go is—" The doctor climbed angrily into the carriage behind Cassius but immediately leaned out again. "Mark my words, Andrew Bingham, in spite of everything, the horseless carriage is going to be with us from now on, and we may as well plan on it. If you're going by the blacksmith shop, will you kindly ask them to haul this noble specimen down and fix it for the twentieth time?"

"There's one supporter, anyway," said Papa as they drove away, "even if he isn't very enthusiastic." He settled back for a comfortable chat, because Peg knew the way

home just as well as he did. "In New York, they have
big busses run by electric batteries to take people sight-
seeing. And in Boston the policemen have a Stanley
Steamer, which runs by steam like a locomotive, to chase
the crooks with. In the end, though, it'll be the gasoline
motors that'll last, even if lots of people are in favor of
steam or electricity right now."

All the way home Papa kept talking—about the Oldsmobile runabout that had been such a sensation at the
1901 Automobile Show last year, about the Frenchman,
Monsieur Fournier, who had won the Paris-to-Berlin automobile race with the astounding speed of forty-seven miles
an hour, and about the people in Detroit and Indianapolis
and Buffalo and goodness knew where else who were building automobiles in bicycle plants or machine shops or sometimes just out in the barn.

"You'd never know it here yet," said Papa, "because
there aren't but the two automobiles in the whole town,
but in the big cities out East it's different, and in France
they've been using automobiles for a good ten years—and
lots of them, too. That's why I think Granite City is a
good place to start—an open field, you might say."

"Start what?" cried Crissy. "You mean you're going to
make automobiles?"

"No," said Papa. "I'm no mechanic, for one thing. Also,

it costs money. My idea is to sell them. You know I can sell things."

Crissy certainly knew that. The reason Papa had been sent to New York to show the Wellfleet line of vehicles at the convention was that he was in charge of selling all the carriages that Mr. Wellfleet made down at the Works. Some of the smaller carriage companies sold mostly by mail from catalogs, but Mr. Wellfleet kept Papa busy all the time talking up the Wellfleet line and making personal calls on dealers all over Michigan and sometimes out of the state, too.

"A real hustler," everybody around town said about Papa. "Why, Bingham could sell an extra pair of ears to a mule!"

"What I want to be is an automobile dealer," Papa went on. "Just automobiles, nothing else."

Crissy knew about the dealers. Some of them had hardware stores or sold farm implements, with carriages and wagons as a sideline, and some of them, in the bigger towns, dealt in nothing but vehicles. This, it seemed, was what Papa had in mind, except that he would sell only automobiles.

"Well, what do you think about it?"

Crissy thought that it would be quite an undertaking, because selling automobiles would take a good deal more persuasion, especially seeing they cost ever so much more money than carriages, besides being, as Aunt Henrietta pointed out, much more dangerous.

"But you can do it," cried Crissy with enthusiasm. "When are you going to start?"

In spite of its all sounding very exciting, Crissy guessed that everybody would not be as delighted as she was. Aunt Henrietta would be cross about Papa suddenly starting out in a new business, and Mr. Wellfleet, down at the Works, would be crosser still, because he wouldn't want to lose Papa.

"Besides everybody in town saying you're crazy to give up a good job that way," she said, out loud this time. "Oh, dear, I'm going to have to do a lot of arguing at school!"

"You may be my assistant salesman," said Papa grandly. "I'll teach you all the talking points, and you can use them on anybody that says I'm crazy. You might even convince one or two—that I'm not, I mean." He looked at her sober face. "Not scared, are you?"

Crissy shook her head.

"No, sir!" she said stoutly. "What's there to be scared of?"

"That's my girl!" said Papa. "I knew I could depend on you. However, to bolster you up in moments of doubt, I'll give you a thought to hold. Now, let me see—"

Peg turned neatly into the drive, stopped in front of the barn, and looked inquiringly over her shoulder at Papa.

"Yes, yes," said Papa. "Just give me a minute to think."

Peg stamped her foot, but Papa still sat in the surrey and thought. Peg stamped her foot harder and whinnied loudly.

"Thank you, Peg," said Papa. "Now I have it.

'No matter what the horses say,
The automobile's here to stay.'

All right, Peg, you may go in and get your supper."

He climbed briskly down, opened the barn door and led Peg in. Susan-Cat jumped down, too, and eased over to her favorite mousehole. Crissy looked the surrey over carefully for cat hairs, picked off half a dozen, and went to measure out Peg's oats.

"No matter what the horses say,
The automobile's here to stay,"

she chanted, making up a little matching tune as she went along.

Papa grinned and joined in.

"It's a good verse," said Crissy as they walked up to the house. "You can change the words in the middle if you want to."

"So you can," said Papa, squeezing her hand.

Crissy was pretty sure that Papa knew that she was busy changing the verse to read,

"No matter what Aunt Hen may say,
The automobile's here to stay."

2

YOU MAKE 'EM,
I'LL SELL 'EM!

Papa and Crissy were pedaling down to the Carriage Works on Papa's bicycle. At least, Papa was pedaling, and Crissy was riding on the handlebars.

"The idea! A big girl like you!" Aunt Henrietta had sputtered. "Really, Andrew, I just seem to be making a little progress with her, when you manage to undo it all."

But Papa had only smiled his easy smile and said, "Don't expect us home this noon, Hen. We'll eat at the Dutton

House and save you some work."

The reason Papa liked to eat at the Dutton House was because it was right across from the ten-cent sheds, where the farmers always left their horses and wagons while they did their Saturday shopping. Most of them went across to the Dutton House at noon to eat the big twenty-five-cent dinner, to talk about the crops, and to listen to Papa describing the latest in road carts and carriages.

"I've sold a lot of surreys by eating at the Dutton House," said Papa.

He didn't add that he hoped to sell a lot of automobiles the same way, because Aunt Henrietta had just about worn herself out arguing and fussing about his changing jobs, and there was no use getting her started again. Papa simply clapped his stiff straw hat on his head, said "All ready, Crissy," and walked out of the house. Crissy marched out behind him, with a little swagger to show that she was on Papa's side.

Crissy waved to Elmo as she and Papa whizzed past on the bicycle. For once in her life, she was actually sorry for Elmo, because his father wasn't the first automobile dealer in Granite City—nor ever could be, now that Papa was already it. Suddenly a new problem struck her.

"Papa," she said, "where are you going to get the automobiles to sell?"

Papa chuckled.

"I wondered when you'd think of that. I have a little scheme to get the automobiles, though it may not work worth a nickel. If it doesn't, we'll have to think up something else."

That was every word that she could get out of him until he whirled the bicycle around to the back door of the Carriage Works.

"I want to see the boss," he said. "You can go and watch Jed Haley paint stripes if you want to."

Naturally, Crissy wanted to, although she thought perhaps she ought to be with Papa while Mr. Wellfleet scolded him for quitting his job, which she supposed was what Papa had come for. Crissy always preferred having sympathetic company while she was being scolded, but she guessed that men didn't want little girls around while they argued about things.

She stepped into the big shop, which looked like three barns and a few chicken coops all strung together and divided into sections by doors which sometimes stood open and sometimes were tightly closed. She sniffed happily at the wonderful mixture of smells. Scorched wood from the blacksmith shop, timber from the wood shop, paint from the paint shop, where coat after coat of paint was put on each carriage and then rubbed down with pumice and water before the next coat went on. And the special odor of a good cigar from the corner where Jed Haley added stripes to the carriages before the final coats of varnish were put on. Jed saw Crissy at once and gestured for her to sit on a box near the carriage which he was striping.

> " 'Hail to thee, blithe Spirit!
> Bird thou never wert,' "

he said. "(Percy Bysshe Shelley, born 1792, died 1822.)"

"Of course I never wert," said Crissy, "though it'd be handy some days when I get tired of walking."

Jed squinted carefully, ran a line of light green along the body of his carriage with a fine camel's-hair brush, and added a handsome curlicue at the end. Crissy gazed in admiration. No wonder, she thought, that everybody wanted to be a striper. Besides the good pay, a striper usually had an interested audience to watch his steady hand put the finishing touches on a stylish carriage.

"Spokes next," said Jed. "What color stripes do you vote for?"

"Red," said Crissy, who thought that everything should be red if possible, even dresses, although Aunt Henrietta insisted that red was not so suitable for little girls as pink or pale blue.

Jed cleaned his brush and selected a new one for the red paint. Suddenly Mr. Wellfleet's roar rose above all the sounds of the Carriage Works.

"Are you crazy?" he shouted. "Of all the hare-brained, half-baked, double-dyed, triple-distilled mistakes—"

Everybody looked anxiously up to Mr. Wellfleet's office, which was a sort of little balcony from which he could peer down every few minutes to see what everybody was doing. He and Papa were hidden now by Mr. Wellfleet's huge rolltop desk, but the conversation flowed out through the whole shop. Crissy expected to see the balcony swaying and rocking with the violence of the argument.

"Wants to be an automobile dealer, if anybody ever heard of such a thing!" Mr. Wellfleet roared. "Best carriage salesman in the state—in the nation maybe—but he wants to take up with a flash-in-the-pan item like an automobile! Sell both, why don't you? Then you won't be out anything while you're coming to your senses."

Papa shook his head.

"Never could keep my mind on two things at once," he said firmly. "When I sell something, I sell that—nothing else."

Mr. Wellfleet went right on roaring.

"Automobiles! You mark my words, in a year the whole thing'll be forgotten. We've had horses for hundreds of years, and no noisy, won't-work invention is going to change that!"

"You may be right," said Papa amiably.

"Right! Of course I'm right!" cried Mr. Wellfleet. "But nobody could prove it to you, I suppose."

"Somebody could, I guess," said Papa in a doubtful voice. "You want to try?"

"Try!" shouted Mr. Wellfleet. "Who'd have to try? It'd be as easy as falling off a log! Why, if you can sell even twenty of those snorting terrors by Jubilee time next summer, I'll—I'll go into the automobile-making business myself!"

"Twenty!" cried Papa. "Of course I can sell twenty—if I can get them."

"Ha! Now he's trying to wiggle his way out, so help me! If he can't get them, he can't sell them, he says. One excuse is as good as another." He pounded on his rolltop desk. "Listen to me! Just so you can't say I put anything in your way, I'll make you twenty of the things—and then sit back and watch you try to sell them!"

"Seems fair enough," said Papa mildly. "Anywhere in particular I have to sell 'em?"

"Sell 'em in Timbuctoo for all I care. Or it might be the Hottentots would take a fancy to 'em."

"Timbuctoo's not practical," said Papa solemnly, "or Hottentots, either. I'll just stick to southern Michigan, where I can demonstrate the product."

"There's a catch to all this," Mr. Wellfleet warned. "If you don't sell those twenty machines by Jubilee time, you're to start selling carriages again, and no more nonsense about automobiles!"

"It's a deal," Papa agreed, not sounding very enthusiastic. "You make 'em; I'll sell 'em. And hurry up and make me a few. I want to get started."

Mr. Wellfleet leaned over the balcony and began calling men from the floor.

"Smith! VanHorn! Dugan! Up here, please!" He turned to Papa. "Never say I didn't put my best men on the job. Not that it's necessary. An automobile is nothing in the world but a carriage with an imitation horse! Get out of here now, and don't bother me. I'll prove to you that the public isn't as rattleheaded as you seem to think!"

Crissy drew a long breath and looked at Jed Haley.

" 'The tumult and the shouting dies;
    The captains and the kings depart,' "

Jed announced solemnly. "(Rudyard Kipling, born 1865 and not dead yet.)"

"Neither am I dead yet," said Papa, striding into the paint shop with his hat at a jaunty angle. "Life, in fact, is just beginning. Jed, you better start practicing on automobile stripes; you're going to be painting plenty of them."

"A stripe's a stripe, no matter what it's on," said Jed. " 'A rose by any other name would smell as sweet.' (William Shakespeare, born—)"

"Born 1564, died 1616," Crissy interrupted glibly. "That's one I know, anyway."

"A pair of literary geniuses," said Papa. "Well, if it isn't too vulgar, let's eat. You come, too, Jed."

Jed shook his head.

"I eat out of a lunch bucket—tasty if not stylish. But at home, if you should be interested, I have an assortment of fine food for the soul. Bring the young lady out some Saturday and make me a visit. I live in the Pinery."

Hardly anyone lived in the Pinery, which was mostly just woods, and the children of Granite City took care not to be caught there after dark, because wild Indians used to live there when it was even more of a wilderness than it was now.

"And maybe some of them still do," Elmo told Crissy once. "Nobody'd know, in all those trees. How'd you like to have an Indian jump out at you?"

Crissy thought that most Indians nowadays were quite tame, and she felt more certain than ever now, since she knew that Jed Haley lived in the Pinery, too. She doubted that all Jed's learning could thrive if surrounded by savage redskins.

She waved good-bye to Jed, who removed his hat from his head and his cigar from his mouth and made her a little bow.

"Well," said Papa, when they were strolling up toward the Dutton House, "I thought I did that quite well. Now we'll have some automobiles to sell, because if Wellfleet says he'll make them, he'll do it."

"You—you mean you had it all figured out?" cried Crissy. "All that arguing and everything?"

Papa nodded solemnly.

"A salesman," he explained, "has to learn how to get people to do what he wants them to. A good salesman does, that is. He has to study out how people are going to act and why, and it's not easy."

"You figured just right on Mr. Wellfleet," said Crissy.

She thought maybe she would like to be a salesman, too, and get Aunt Henrietta to let her slide down banisters and do a lot of other things that she wasn't allowed to.

"I'll watch Papa and see how he manages," she decided.

She had plenty of chances at the Dutton House, because Papa was very busy making himself agreeable to everybody.

Crissy noticed that he always remembered which farmer had wheat in which field, which one had a new grandson, and which lady specialized in chocolate cake and which one in dried-apple pie.

"It's just being interested," she thought, "and that isn't the least bit hard. Only it's hard to speak up and say you're interested."

Today Papa took pains to work in quite a few remarks about automobiles, and this time Crissy was quick to see that most of what he said had something to do with farming.

"They're going to be hauling wheat to market by motor before long," he predicted. "It's quicker, of course, and you can keep your teams working on the farm instead of having to run them into town with the wheat."

"Instead, you run them into town to haul the horseless wagon back home when the motor gives out," muttered one elderly farmer from the depths of a luxuriant gray beard. "No gain that way, that I can see."

"There'll come a day when the people that make automobiles will step right up and fix them when they break down," said Papa, "and there'll come a day, too, when they won't break down very much."

"When either of those days comes, which I don't expect, I'll be waiting with my money in my fist to buy one," said the farmer, "but not before."

"Better start saving then," Papa advised him, "because it might not be as long as you think."

Crissy thought that she would probably have argued with the man and maybe even felt cross and upset, but Papa, she decided, was much too smart. Papa always made people feel as though what they said was worth thinking about even if he didn't agree with them. She was glad when some of the younger men moved down to Papa's end of the big family-style table and started asking questions about automobiles.

Crissy listened, too, although she didn't understand all the talk about one-cylinder and two-cylinder engines, friction clutches, and worm gears. She could see that all she would be able to tell anybody about an automobile would be that it would go faster than a horse and carriage—and that, for Crissy, would be reason enough to buy one.

"And also," she thought triumphantly, "you don't have to feed an automobile when it isn't running or play nursemaid to it, either. That's another good argument, and I thought it up all by myself.

No matter what the horses say,
The automobile's here to stay,"

she murmured to herself and wished that she had a good reason to say it out loud, too.

"Crissy, do you think you could get home by yourself?"

asked Papa when everybody had eaten all they could of firsts and seconds and had pushed their chairs back from the long table. "Henry here wants me to ride out to his place and look over some new machinery he just bought."

Crissy nodded. She would walk home down River Street, stopping to look in the Mercantile at the bolts of plaid gingham for school dresses. She had her eye on some red-and-blue plaid, but she wasn't sure now whether she ought to be thinking about it, seeing that Papa might not sell any automobiles for a while yet.

She was glad that it was Saturday, because there were always so many more people in town on Saturdays, and she was glad, too, that Aunt Henrietta was having another Diamond Jubilee Committee meeting this afternoon, so there would be no hurry about getting home.

Crissy stopped to talk to the Randolph twins, who were in her grade at school. She patted the noses of several horses tied up to hitching posts along River Street. She took a drink from the mineral well which gushed up in its new granite pagoda at the corner by the bank. Crissy was never sure whether she really wanted a drink of the water, which tasted strongly of sulphur, but she could never quite manage to go past without finding out if it really tasted as awful as she had remembered.

"It always does, though," she told herself.

She was just wrinkling her nose over the last swallow

when Elmo came scuffing by. Elmo was always kicking at things, like little rocks and pieces of wood, and he even seemed to be kicking things on River Street, where there was nothing to kick. He came over and took a drink, too.

"Hear you've been horse racing," he said gleefully. "All by yourself, too."

Crissy nodded her head dumbly. So Mrs. Garrett had told, after all! Crissy had hoped so much that Aunt Henrietta would never find out.

"Mrs. Garrett told Mama that she felt it was her duty to tell your Aunt Henrietta," Elmo went on, "only she didn't, because she thought that dear Henrietta had a heavy enough burden to bear."

Crissy let out a long breath of relief, even if she did know that Aunt Henrietta's "burden" meant Crissy and Papa—Crissy because she was a tomboy and not like Martha May, and Papa because he was full of wild ideas like selling automobiles.

"Of course I could tell your Aunt Henrietta myself," Elmo said, "but maybe I won't if you wheel the baby to-morrow."

"All right." Crissy got tired of wheeling the baby so much, but it would be worth it this time to have Elmo keep still about the racing, because if Aunt Henrietta found out, she was as apt as not to decide that Crissy couldn't drive Peg at all. "You wait, though, Elmo Hawkins! When

Papa gets a horseless carriage, I won't give you even one little ride!"

"One little walk, you mean!" Elmo retorted. "Those things don't run worth a nickel, not one of them. Everybody always has to walk home!"

Crissy started to splutter and argue, but then she remembered that maybe Elmo's father might want to buy an automobile some day, so she decided to try some salesmanship instead.

"An automobile would certainly come in handy in case —in case your horse went lame," she declared, saying the first thing that popped into her head, "or if you needed a doctor right away, or if—"

But Elmo was already on the other side of the street, looking at the Hardware's line of fishing poles. Crissy went across the iron bridge over the Granite River and leaned over the railing to look down into its murky depths. There wasn't much water there right now, because it had been a dry summer, but Papa was always telling about how the river came up one spring right over the bank and right over the bridge, too, and started flowing down River Street just as though it belonged there.

Crissy heard a roaring and a snorting in the street beside her, and then Dr. Agnew's brusque voice.

"Thinking about falling in? If so, kindly do it now while medical attention is at hand."

"Oh, no, sir," said Crissy, "though it would be a nice day to fall into something. Aunt Henrietta won't let me do anything but wade."

And why, Crissy wondered as soon as she had said it, did she have to mention Aunt Henrietta to Dr. Agnew, of all people? The doctor didn't seem to notice, though.

"I have a patient to see just down the block from your house," he said, "so if you're going home, I'd be pleased to have you ride with me."

"In—in your automobile?"

Crissy was almost speechless with joy.

"I hope so," said Dr. Agnew. "For the moment, at least, we'll ride in my automobile. Cassius and Rex aren't far away, though."

Crissy was so much excited that she forgot to notice how Dr. Agnew made the horseless carriage go, although she did remember afterward that he steered with a sort of a handle and that there was a great deal of clanking which seemed to come from under the seat. She didn't suppose that they actually went as fast as she and Peg had gone the day before, but it seemed faster because of the strange noises from the engine.

"I can't really let it out," Dr. Agnew shouted, "because the chief of police says he'll arrest anybody who goes faster than a horse can trot."

"He didn't say what horse, did he?" asked Crissy. "Peg

can go quite fast, and Papa says that big horse of Mr. Dryden's ran a mile in two minutes and twenty seconds once."

"I believe you have a point there," Dr. Agnew agreed, "but I don't think it would be wise to argue it out with the chief."

Crissy sat up straight and tried to look as large as possible so that nobody she knew would miss the sight of Crissy Bingham riding in an automobile with Dr. Agnew. It was too bad that Elmo was still downtown, but maybe Martha May might see her.

"Did you know that Papa's going to sell automobiles?" Crissy shouted above increased roaring from the motor.

Dr. Agnew nodded.

"Tell him if this one of mine breaks down completely, I'll buy one from him," he said. "If his is any good, I mean."

"Mr. Wellfleet's going to make them, so I guess they'll be all right. Only he's not making them to be nice; he's making them to get Papa to give up the idea. He says it's all a double-dyed mistake."

"Everybody's entitled to his own opinion," said Dr. Agnew, "including me. Tell your papa I said to stick to it. He's young and has some years to waste. Well, well, here we are at your front door."

He stamped on some pedals on the floor of the automobile and stopped so abruptly that Crissy almost went out over the dashboard. She climbed down reluctantly.

"Thank you very much," she said, yelling above the sound of the motor. "It—it was just wonderful. Nobody I know ever rode in one, except Papa, and I think it's lovely."

"The pleasure was all mine," said Dr. Agnew, but he smiled at Crissy to tell her that he knew some of it was hers too. "It—"

"Clarissa Jane!" Aunt Henrietta came running down from the porch. "Is something the matter? You aren't sick?"

"No, ma'am," said Crissy blissfully. "Dr. Agnew just gave me a ride home."

"How do you do, Henrietta?" said Dr. Agnew in a voice that sounded rather full of lemons.

"V-very well, thank you, Chauncey. How good of you to bring Clarissa Jane home!"

"Not at all. Glad to be of assistance."

Dr. Agnew put his hat back on and roared off down the street. Crissy hardly noticed him, because she was staring at Aunt Henrietta.

"Why, she's young!" Crissy thought. "Or almost. And she's blushing, just like anybody."

She was astonished to see that Aunt Henrietta blushing was quite pretty—not at all the way she looked when she was thinking about what was proper and what wasn't.

"Dear me, I wonder why she didn't marry him!"

Crissy smoothed her blown hair in front of the hall mirror. She was so much interested in thinking about Dr. Agnew and Aunt Henrietta that she didn't even protest when Aunt Henrietta shooed her into the parlor to make her manners to the Diamond Jubilee ladies. Crissy thought that it was silly to start worrying already about a Jubilee that wouldn't be until next summer, but that was the way Aunt Henrietta was—always determined to have everything planned so it would come out just so.

Even the parlor was just so, exactly like a picture that Aunt Henrietta had cut out of a magazine. The embroidered pillows on the couch were plumped up, the lace curtains stood out stiffly, the portieres were draped back in exact curves, the wicker rockers stood rigidly in their proper corners, and even the cattails on the upright piano were arranged so that they spread from their hand-painted vase like a perfect fan.

"Dear Henrietta! I don't see how she manages to do all she does!" exclaimed Mrs. Garrett to the other ladies. "Oh, Clarissa Jane! How do you do today? I do hope you can come to play with Martha May soon."

"Thank you very much," said Crissy in her politest voice, knowing that Mrs. Garrett probably didn't hope any such thing. "I'll be rather busy now, though, helping Papa. He's going to sell automobiles, you know."

"Yes, I know," said Mrs. Garrett in a tone that implied that this was really the worst. "I wonder who in the world will buy them."

Crissy could feel herself bristling, but she remembered about salesmanship just in time.

"Oh, everybody, I'm sure," she said amiably. "Most of the stylish people in New York have them, and Papa says it won't be any time at all until everybody in Granite City does, too." She gazed innocently around at the circle of doubtful faces. "All the important people, anyway."

Aunt Henrietta appeared at the door with the tea tray, and Crissy jumped up to help her.

"Yes, indeed," said Crissy with a sudden inspiration. "Why, there'll even be automobiles in the Diamond Jubilee parade, and I'll be riding in one, too!"

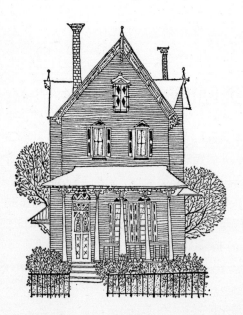

3

GET A HORSE!

Crissy scuffed through the yellow maple leaves on the way home from school and sniffed absent-mindedly at a bonfire burning in Elmo's back yard. October was lovely, but it would be much lovelier if Mr. Wellfleet would hurry up and get Papa some automobiles to sell. Elmo leaned on his rake and looked gloomy.

"You going to Martha May's Halloween party?" he asked.

Crissy nodded.

"Me, too," said Elmo. "Mama says I have to, and right on Halloween night, too, when I could be having some fun around town."

"Maybe we could leave early," said Crissy. "Papa always lets me go out a little while on Halloween night."

"What do you mean, we?" asked Elmo. "Who wants a girl tagging along?"

"You wouldn't want your mother to know you didn't stay for the whole party, would you?" asked Crissy innocently. "And you wouldn't want everybody to know what your middle name is, either."

"You don't know what it is yourself," argued Elmo with horror.

"Don't I?" said Crissy softly. "I think you should go to the party as Little Lord Fauntleroy. Of course, you'd have to have a wig with golden curls, and a black velvet suit and a lace collar like the outfit Martha May wore last Halloween, and—"

"All right, all right." Crissy was glad to see that Elmo knew when he was beaten. "We'll both leave early. We might make us a couple of tick-tacks to take along."

"Let's." Crissy thought there was nothing like a tick-tack to make a dreadful noise, which naturally was what a person wanted on Halloween. "I can bring some corn to throw, too. Peg won't miss a little."

Crissy scuffed on toward home. When Papa came back from the convention, it had looked as though there would be considerable excitement on account of his selling automobiles. Instead, except for a lot of arguments that Crissy had gotten into with people who said Papa was crazy to mix in the horseless carriage business, things had been just about as usual. Papa was still selling carriages until he could get some automobiles, Crissy was going to school all week and wrangling with Elmo on Saturdays, Aunt Henrietta was having Diamond Jubilee Committee meetings, and Granite City still had two automobiles and no more.

"Except for Mr. Wellfleet's, which doesn't count," Crissy grumbled.

Mr. Wellfleet, much to Crissy's annoyance, had suddenly developed a pride which would not let him put even one automobile on the market until it had been tested in every way he could think of.

"Going to have my name on it, isn't it?" he demanded. "Can't have my name on something that's no good, can I? Don't want people bringing them back, do I? If anybody buys one, that is."

And so Mr. Wellfleet's automobile was being driven over all the bumpiest roads around Granite City, up the worst hills, and down the steepest inclines. Mr. Wellfleet even talked a little about pushing it off the Third Street hill into the Flats to see how it would hold up, but Papa finally persuaded him to give up that notion. He never could persuade him, though, to stay off the oozy country roads on rainy days.

"Have to see what she'll do," said Mr. Wellfleet stubbornly.

"If only he'd see by himself," Papa complained when he arrived home one day liberally spattered with mud, "but he's bound I'll ride along and see, too."

Crissy would have been happy to ride along herself, mud or no mud, but if Papa went, there was never enough room for Crissy because Mr. Wellfleet had refused so far to even think about putting a motor in anything but a one-seated buggy.

"If the thing blows up, which it's apt to do any minute, I'm not going to be out so much," he said gloomily.

"People with families will have to have two-seaters," Papa argued.

"With families!" roared Mr. Wellfleet. "Who'd be foolish enough to risk his family in one of those noisy, dirty things?"

"I would," said Papa, winking at Crissy.

Mr. Wellfleet threw up his hands.

"When you get an order for a two-seater," he said, "I'll make one—and not before."

"I can't get orders with nothing to sell," Papa reminded him.

"There you go again!" cried Mr. Wellfleet in a rage. "A man can't build a good product in fifteen minutes."

"And a man can't sell twenty cars in fifteen minutes, either," said Papa, "which is about what I'm going to have to do if you don't get a move on."

On such days Crissy could see the weeks passing and Papa losing his chance to be an automobile dealer and to have the nice showroom which he had described in great detail to Crissy.

"But that's for later," he told her, "when I get those twenty machines sold. After that I'll be a real dealer. The Bingham Motor Company, we'll call it."

"Done in gold on the glass," Crissy sighed. "Oh, Papa!"

In the meantime, it stood to reason that Papa couldn't sell automobiles with snow on the ground, which there would be before long, maybe even in November if it was an early winter.

"Between snowy roads and frozen-up motors, nobody even thinks of driving in cold weather," Papa explained. "About all I can do is to call on some of the out-of-town vehicle dealers, but most of them won't order an automobile sight unseen, if at all, and they certainly can't see them before spring unless they come on the train to take a look. So mostly in good weather I'll have to do my selling close enough at hand so I can drive a machine to show, and I wouldn't want to try that any farther away than about thirty miles in each direction."

Thirty miles in each direction seemed like plenty of distance to Crissy, because it would take Papa into several other counties besides Granite County. But not being able to do any real demonstrating until at least March would give him only four months at the most to sell his twenty machines before the Diamond Jubilee.

The Jubilee was going to be combined with the Fourth of July celebration, because nobody was sure exactly when Jeremiah Hannibal, the first permanent settler, had come to Granite City. There was even a lot of argument about which year it was, but the committee figured they had hit it within a year or two and that probably the Hannibal family had arrived in the summer, which was the only fit time to travel in those days. Aunt Henrietta had fussed some because of not knowing exactly, but she finally joined with the rest of the committee in ordering banners that read "Granite City Diamond Jubilee, 1828-1903."

Crissy scuffed on as far as the corner, smoothed down her hair, polished her shoes hastily on the back of her black stockings, and went in by the kitchen door. Aunt Henrietta, looking pink from the heat of the oven, was baking sugar cookies. Crissy bit into a hot one.

"You can get yourself a glass of milk down cellar,"

said Aunt Henrietta, "and then you better run upstairs and change out of your school clothes."

"Yes, ma'am."

Crissy had felt quite different about Aunt Henrietta after seeing her blush at Dr. Agnew that day.

"He's probably lonely in that great big house," said Crissy.

"Who?" asked Aunt Henrietta.

Crissy jumped. She hadn't meant to say it out loud, so she pretended she hadn't heard and leaned over to pet Susan-Cat, who was waiting for a bite of cookie.

"It's too bad you're not black," Crissy told Susan. "I'd be a witch at Martha May's party, and you could ride on my broomstick."

"She could be the ghost of a witch's cat," said Aunt Henrietta unexpectedly, "which would be even spookier."

"Why, it would be wonderful!" cried Crissy, astonished at such a flight of fancy from Aunt Henrietta.

All the way upstairs, she wondered whether Aunt Henrietta ever thought about Dr. Agnew and whether she was sorry that he had never married but had to live all alone except for old Mrs. Jenkins, who came in to cook his meals and keep the house clean. Why, Aunt Henrietta might have been living in that house all these years instead of going away to college and teaching school and, now, looking out for Crissy and Papa. It gave Crissy a sad feeling to think of it, although probably Aunt Henrietta didn't mind or she would have married Dr. Agnew in the first place.

"Clarissa Jane!" Aunt Henrietta called up the stairs in the voice that meant she didn't approve of something. "Your father is here and wants you to go with him."

Crissy listened to the thudding of a motor outside and then scurried down the stairs. Papa had the Wellfleet sitting out in front, shivering violently with the vibration of the motor.

"Mr. Wellfleet wants this tested on Windmill Hill," said Papa, "and I thought you might as well go along."

"Will you be home for supper?" asked Aunt Henrietta. Papa grinned at her.

"Time will tell," he said. "Better fix something that'll keep. Come on, Crissy."

"It must be an experience, anyway," said Aunt Henrietta, "though I must say—"

"Why, Aunt Henrietta wants to go, too," thought Crissy in astonishment. "Only she's too stubborn to say so."

Crissy pulled at Papa's coat.

"Papa—" she began, but Papa kept on going out the door.

"Motor's liable to stop," he said.

They were almost to the edge of town before something stirred between Crissy and Papa, and Susan-Cat stuck her head out from under a greasy old rag.

"Oh, Papa!" cried Crissy. "She must have thought it was the carriage without Peg hitched on yet." Susan sat up straight and purred. "She wants to go faster."

"I can't think what I'm going to do with the two of you," Papa grumbled. "Next thing you'll both want to go up in a skyrocket because it's faster."

As Papa kept speeding the Wellfleet up, Crissy sat forward in excitement, clutching the side of the carriage with one hand and Susan-Cat with the other. She felt as though her ears were blowing off, and she knew that one hair ribbon was sailing down the road far behind.

"How fast?" she asked.

"Maybe twenty miles an hour," Papa yelled.

Crissy gasped. That was almost as fast as Mr. Dryden's race horse ever went. Why, twenty miles was all the way to Cassville, a trip that took the whole morning even if Peg was in a hurry to get there.

"Papa," cried Crissy above the sound of the motor, "Aunt Henrietta wanted to come, too."

"I know," said Papa, "but if I'd asked her this time she wouldn't have come. Wait until about ten times from now, and maybe it'll be different. Maybe not, too. Hen has to work into things gradually, if at all. Well, here comes our hill."

Windmill Hill was so steep that people around Granite City were willing to drive a couple of miles out of their way

to keep from going up it, and those who had to go that
way usually got out and walked to make the load lighter for
the horses. Crissy wondered if maybe she should get out
and walk, too, but Papa never even hesitated. He made
the engine roar a little louder and sailed straight up. Almost at the top, the motor coughed a couple of times, and
Crissy leaned forward to help it go ahead. The Wellfleet
bucked violently and struggled just over the crest of the
hill before the motor died completely, leaving a disagree-
able little echo behind it.

"Well, we made it," said Papa, "but I thought for a
minute there that I'd have to throw Susan overboard to
lighten the load."

Two farm boys with a wagon and team came tearing
down the road, yelled "Get a horse!" and went on down
the hill without even hesitating. Papa cranked the motor
a few times in vain and finally pushed the Wellfleet around
until it was facing the way they had come.

"A little coasting party," he said, giving the machine
a final shove and leaping in just as it started to swoop
down the hill. "A down grade helps turn the motor over
sometimes."

Halfway down, Papa managed to get the motor started
again, and they went flying off toward home.

"No need to eat all that dust up ahead," said Papa as
they came into the edge of town, where the brick sidewalks

began. "We can pass any team of horses as though they were tied."

"Maybe it isn't horses inside that cloud of dust," said Crissy.

"Might be a dragon, I suppose." Papa speeded up the motor and started to go around. "Or a herd of elephants. It might even be— Hey! It's Jed in another Wellfleet!"

Through the dust, Crissy heard a familiar voice.

"Get a horse!" Elmo yelled tauntingly from the sidewalk. "Get a horse!"

"Jed's being towed!" cried Crissy.

Papa shut off the gasoline so hastily that his machine backfired violently. The team of horses pulling Jed's Wellfleet reared, lunged, and ran away, hauling Jed and his machine alternately on the road and in the ditch until the traces parted and the horses vanished in their own cloud of dust. They were pursued by their red-faced driver, who had been jerked from his seat beside Jed and was now running on his heels, yanking back on the reins with all his might.

"Told you those horseless carriages were always making trouble," said Elmo, setting down the basket of apples which he was carrying. "Here, have one. I walked out to Grandpa's and got 'em."

Crissy looked at him indignantly as Papa got out to talk to Jed.

"This machine's not making any trouble, is it?" she asked coldly. "And you can keep your old apples." She went over to join Papa and Jed. "You aren't hurt, are you?"

Jed climbed calmly out of his machine and looked at it critically.

"Neither it nor me," he said. " 'Think you, a little din can daunt mine ears? Have I not in my time heard lions roar?' (William Shakespeare, born and died you know when.)"

"We'd better get you out of that ditch," said Papa.

"Never should have gotten in," said Jed disgustedly. "I'm a striper, not a test driver, but try to tell Wellfleet that! 'O Duty!' (William Wordsworth, born 1770, died 1850.)"

Anyway, Crissy was glad to see that Mr. Wellfleet had put a motor in another carriage, so that eventually, she supposed, Papa would have at least two to sell.

After everybody had pushed and tugged in vain, Papa tied a rope from his machine to Jed's and, with much clanking and roaring, hauled the ditched automobile back on the road. The motor on Jed's machine still refused to start.

"Might as well haul you on down to the Works," Papa decided. "Elmo, you can climb in and ride with Jed if you want to."

Crissy scowled over her shoulder at Elmo.

" 'Get a horse,' huh?" she yelled as the little procession started off. "Get an automobile, you mean!"

She was so proud of the performance of Papa's Wellfleet that she decided to use automobiling as an idea for her Halloween costume. She had seen an article in the newspaper that told how ladies in New York dressed for driving, and she had also found a piece from Paris in one of Aunt Henrietta's fashion magazines.

"A simple costume is best for the automobilist," the magazine advised its feminine readers. "Leave your Sunday hat at home and wear a simple sailor, trimmed, at most, with a wreath of flowers or a few plumes. Tie your headgear firmly in place with a veil. Goggles will keep your eyes bright for the end of the trip or, if you prefer, simply tie the veil over your face as well as your hat, and leave the goggles at home. Cover your frock with a duster, the long linen coat which is the newest in motoring fashions, and take to the open road."

Crissy decided on goggles, because they would disguise her more completely, and she found a huge flowered hat and a length of chiffon veiling in the attic. For her duster she used an old tan coat of Aunt Henrietta's.

"Very clever," said Papa when Crissy started off for Martha May's. "There's nothing like keeping people thinking about automobiles."

Crissy hoped that people would think about the Wellfleet that ran instead of the one that didn't, but in any case she was bound to show that she was faithful to automobiles. She kissed Papa and Aunt Henrietta good-bye and went out to the barn to shell some of Peg's corn. She did hope that Elmo had remembered to make the tick-tacks. Tick-tacks were easy enough—just a nail to stick under the siding of the victim's house and to hold a long string, drawn taut and rubbed with a chunk of rosin, which was what made all the racket. Crissy loaded her pockets with corn and hurried along the street and up on the Garretts' lighted front porch.

"Abandon hope, all ye who enter here," said a sepulchral voice which Crissy immediately recognized as belonging to Martha May's big brother, who was in high school. Wrapped in a sheet, he extended a clammy hand for Crissy to shake.

"Wet sand in an old kid glove," thought Crissy scornfully, but she remembered to give a little shriek of terror.

Everybody was sitting stiffly on the Garretts' chairs, speaking only when necessary and then in disguised voices. The costumes were about as usual, Crissy noted—a clown, a ghost, a witch, an angel, who was of course Martha May because of her golden hair, a Spanish girl, a pair of Indians, and— Crissy smothered a gurgle of laughter. That was certainly a horse sitting in the chair in the farthest corner—a horse with a silly, smirking face, a spotted hide, and a long tail that dragged on the floor behind.

"Somebody's old bell pull, plus somebody's hair switch," thought Crissy as she inspected the strange tail with its luxuriant hair at the end. "Well, horses and automobilists certainly go together, at least as long as automobiles have to be hauled home as much as they do."

Crissy settled herself on a chair beside the horse and waited patiently for the games to begin. She knew that they would play pin the tail on the donkey, spin the plate, and bobbing for apples, because that was what everybody else did at their parties.

"And so Martha May and Mrs. Garrett will too," Crissy thought.

She didn't mind much, because games were fun, no matter how many times you played them, but on Halloween it would be nice to be surprised.

"Baseball, maybe," she remarked to the horse, "or pitching quoits."

"In here?" said the horse in a mincing voice. "Scratched furniture, busted knickknacks, cracked mirrors."

"Now, children," said Mrs. Garrett from the doorway, "I want you all to march past me while I judge the best costumes. Then we will unmask and have the games. Spin the plate, pin the tail on the donkey—"

"Ha!" said the horse. "Same old thing. How soon do you think we can get out of here?"

"Elmo!" cried Crissy. "It's you!"

"Naturally," said Elmo, galloping past Mrs. Garrett and switching his unwieldy tail. "Who'd you think it was? I suppose you forgot the corn."

Crissy pointed wordlessly to her bulging pockets.

"Unmask now, children," said Mrs. Garrett, "and we will give out the prizes for the best costumes and start our games."

Elmo got a prize, and so did Crissy.

"She's dying to give one to Martha May, too," Elmo whispered, "but she dasn't."

Crissy nodded. She was tired of being polite, and Martha May, who was making sprightly conversation with everybody, set her teeth on edge even more than usual tonight. She thought longingly of the cool dark outside and of the scurrying, giggling children who did not have to go to parties but might scour the town in search of excitement.

"I think your costume is sweet," said Martha May in the gushing voice that sounded exactly like her mother's.

"Yours, too," said Crissy briefly.

"Mama says it's so funny of you to be so set on automobiles," Martha May continued in honeyed tones. "None of the girls we know are, especially since they're just a fad.

But, of course, with your father so crazy about them, I don't suppose— Oh, excuse me, I have to speak to Mama."

Crissy exchanged a glance with Elmo as they stood waiting their turn at the big washtub that was set in the middle of the dining room floor for the apple bobbing.

"I could trip over your foot and push her in when she starts bobbing for apples," Elmo whispered. "Accidentally, of course."

It was a great temptation, but Crissy managed to resist it and to say, "Oh, Elmo, I don't think—" But Elmo was already strutting around the room, with the bedraggled tail swishing along on the floor behind him. Two or three other boys, to whom he had confided that mischief was brewing, clustered around him until Martha May came to take her place at the apple bobbing. Elmo tiptoed carefully up behind her as she knelt beside the tub, but he turned his back and put on his most innocent expression when he saw Mrs. Garrett coming into the room with a big cut-glass pitcher of cider.

"Now then, children," she began, "let's all— Oh!"

She stepped on the end of Elmo's horse tail, tripped over the middle of it, and clutched Elmo to save herself from falling. The cider sprayed over Martha May's bent golden head, and Elmo sat abruptly in the washtub among the few remaining apples.

"Oh, my!"

Crissy tried to look properly horrified, but finally she gave up, muffled her face in her veil, and shook with smothered laughter. Elmo did look so funny sitting helplessly in

the washtub, and Martha May looked just as funny with cider dripping down into her eyes.

"Serves her right for talking mean about Papa and his automobiles!" thought Crissy, gazing with satisfaction at Martha May's lank hair. "There isn't even a bend in that hair now, and Mrs. Garrett always said it was naturally curly!"

Crissy didn't even try to keep from laughing when Mrs.

Garrett brought Elmo back after outfitting him with dry clothes.

"It looked as though he'd have to wear one of Martha May's dresses," Mrs. Garrett explained, "but then I remembered her Little Lord Fauntleroy costume from last Halloween. I do think it looks sweet. So lucky we had it!"

"Sweet!" raged Elmo as he and Crissy managed to slide out through the side door in the middle of a game of blind-man's buff and join the Harris girls and their little brother outside. "Sweet! Here, hold my horse costume while I tuck this lace collar inside. Velvet pants and a lace collar!"

Elmo soon forgot his troubles as the children skirmished around all the houses in the block, leaping at every moving shadow. They threw corn on the porch of Miss Williams, who was so clean that she always washed the doorknobs as soon as company left. They attached a tick-tack under the siding on the house of Mr. Wolf, who had once thrown a stone at Susan-Cat. Crissy held her ears in delight as Elmo, from behind the fence, rubbed rosin on the tick-tack string.

"Oooh! What an awful noise!" cried Crissy. "Sounds as though we were ripping the siding right off the house. Elmo! Here he comes! Skiddoo!"

They scurried in delicious terror down alleys, around houses, and over hedges until Mr. Wolf's following footsteps faded in the distance.

"Whe-ew!" Crissy panted. "That was a run, all right. Where'll we go now?"

"Nowhere, I guess," said Elmo with regret. "Hear that?"

The slow notes of the town clock boomed out over the dark streets.

"Nine o'clock," said Crissy. "I have to go home, too. And we have another tick-tack left. We could put it on your house."

Elmo shook his head.

"Baby's asleep. The only thing that makes Mama really mad is for somebody to wake the baby up."

"I guess we better just keep it until next year then," Crissy decided. "We could put it on our house, but Aunt Henrietta might get asking then if I stayed at the party all the time. Here, you carry your horse costume awhile now. It's heavy."

The porch light was on when they came to Crissy's house, and Papa was standing on the steps with Jed Haley.

"Here she is!" said Papa. "Our little automobilist! And who's that carrying the horse?"

Crissy giggled.

"You know it's Elmo, Papa."

Papa pretended to look more closely.

"So it is, so it is," he agreed. "I've heard of horses carrying people, but not the other way around."

"Had a little accident," said Elmo grumpily. "G'night."

At the gate he looked back at Crissy. "You didn't have to laugh quite so hard, did you?"

"I'm sorry," said Crissy. "I did try not to."

But Elmo had disappeared toward home.

"Jed, you're sure you won't come in?" Papa invited.

"My cigar and I seldom go indoors," said Jed. "The ladies don't like us."

"I'm a lady, and I do," said Crissy.

"A statement I'll cherish."

Jed ceremoniously tipped his hat.

"He stopped by to say that Mr. Wellfleet is satisfied with one machine, and so I may start selling it," Papa said jubilantly. "No more carriages for me!"

" 'Say not the struggle nought availeth,' " remarked Jed as he mounted his bicycle at the curb. "(Arthur Hugh Clough, born 1819, died 1861.) Good evening, friends. I should perhaps be riding a broomstick tonight instead of a bicycle."

"Oh, Papa!" Crissy hurled herself at her father. "Now you can begin. You're a really, truly automobile salesman!"

"Nothing else but," said Papa solemnly. "The latest model salesman, too, complete with automobile."

4

THE PINERY

"Stop it!" cried Crissy. "You act like a wooden Indian!"

Elmo continued to say nothing, pointing annoyingly to one of the large collection of celluloid buttons which covered his lapels and most of the front of his coat. This particular button said "Is *that* so?" He had greeted her on the way to school by pointing to a button that said "Hello, Bright Eyes," and now on the way home he was still continuing his silent conversation.

Crissy could see why Elmo was proud of his collection
of lapel buttons. He had more than any other boy at school,
partly because he had two young uncles who were always
bringing him new and unusual ones from Detroit and partly
because Elmo was an extra good trader. Crissy decided
to try to break the silence by flattery.

"I wish you'd tell me how you got them all," she remarked. "I think you're terribly smart."

Elmo grinned and pointed to a button that announced
"You said a mouthful." Crissy could have kicked him in
the shins. Instead she poked an angry finger at the button
that said "You've got bats in your belfry" and swished off
toward home.

She had wanted to tell Elmo all about the wonderful idea
she had for a Thanksgiving play with one of Papa's automobiles in it, but if he was going to be so horrid about not
saying a word she guessed he could just wait a while to
find out about it.

Crissy thought it was the luckiest thing in the world
that the teacher had chosen her to write the play for the

parents' program, because it would be a wonderful opportunity to call the attention of all the mamas and papas to the advantages of owning an automobile, if Crissy could only think of a way to work an automobile in.

"I did think Elmo might help," she sputtered to herself, "but with nothing on his mind but those old buttons—Oh, Papa, you're home!"

"I couldn't see that farmer who was asking about an automobile," said Papa. "He had to go to a funeral."

Papa didn't sound exactly discouraged, because he was never that, but Crissy did think he was a little disappointed not to have sold a machine right away. Both he and Crissy had felt that as soon as one was ready to be sold the excitement would begin and everybody would want one.

"Wantin' and gittin's two different things," one old man had told Papa. "It's a lot of money for some newfangled outfit that might work and might not."

"The Wellfleet's guaranteed," Papa had argued. "If it doesn't work, bring it back and your money will be cheerfully refunded."

"I'll just wait until spring, anyway," the old man had insisted, "and I ain't saying what spring, either."

"Oh, well, there's always another day," Papa said now. "I thought we might go out to the Pinery and see Jed tomorrow. He keeps asking us to come, and Saturday afternoon's a good time for everybody."

"That'll be nice," said Crissy. "I'll just go in and start the dusting now, so it'll be done by then."

Ever since Halloween, Aunt Henrietta had made Crissy do all the dusting, upstairs and down, because Mrs. Garrett had rushed over right after the party to tell Aunt Henrietta that Crissy had left early without so much as a thank you. Also, Aunt Henrietta had looked at Crissy very queerly when she heard about the unfortunate accident which had befallen Martha May.

"It was her own mother that poured cider on her," Crissy protested silently, "and knocked Elmo into the washtub besides, so I don't see why Aunt Henrietta looks at me."

All the same, it seemed a good idea to give Aunt Henrietta nothing more to complain about.

"You'd make a good dust cloth," Crissy told Susan-Cat, who leaped guiltily down from Aunt Henrietta's best gilded chair when Crissy came into the parlor, "if only your hair didn't come off."

Crissy picked up the vase of cattails, carried it out on the front porch, and blew on it as hard as she could, being careful not to move a single cattail out of the place where Aunt Henrietta had arranged it. She lifted all the photographs off the top of the piano and dusted under them. She ran her dust cloth through the elaborately carved spindles of the wicker chairs to make sure that no speck of dust should escape her. She even stood on a chair and painfully dusted the fancy open scrollwork that filled in the top and sides of the big archway.

"There! That's done!"

She was ready now for the dining room, which wasn't bad except that she had to crawl around on the floor to dust the lion's-paw legs on the huge oval table and the fancy rounds on the chairs. She was glad that she was not expected to climb up and dust the plate rail, which was lined with hand-painted plates, some done by Aunt Henrietta and others brought back by the family or friends from visits all over the country.

One plate which Crissy particularly admired had *Chicago World's Fair, 1893* painted in gold letters on an exciting background of scenes from the fair. And then there was the set of dinner plates, each decorated with different fruits and flowers, which Aunt Henrietta had painted when she was engaged to Dr. Agnew. There were a few cups and saucers to match in the china closet, but Aunt Henrietta had never finished the set. Crissy thought that these "honeymoon dishes" gave an interesting air of lost romance to the dining room.

After the dining room, Crissy would have to dust the bedrooms, but she decided to do them tomorrow morning while Aunt Henrietta was sweeping the parlor carpet with

a wet broom to keep the dust from flying. Aunt Henrietta
looked much less stern than usual with a towel tied around
her head and little strands of hair curling out as she flew
around the house in search of dirt, and Crissy always felt
more comfortable with her at such times.

"We'll stop by the Works a minute on our way," Papa
said the next day when they had eaten their usual Saturday
noon dinner of Boston baked beans and brown bread. "I
want to try a new trick on this motor while there's nobody
to bother me."

It seemed queer to Crissy to walk into the shop and
find nobody there except Mr. Wellfleet, who blinked down
at them from his little balcony and then went back to his
bookkeeping. He always checked the books on Saturday
afternoons after the bookkeeper had gone home, and on
one momentous occasion he had found an error of eleven
cents, whereupon he had driven to the bookkeeper's house
in a rage and had brought that hapless man back down
to the shop to locate the error.

"You can wander around," Papa told Crissy. "I'll be in
the automobile shop."

The automobile shop was nothing but another little
room which Mr. Wellfleet had had partitioned off for the
men who were working on Papa's machines.

"Just throw up any kind of a wall," he told the workmen.

"Something I can take down easy, because it won't be needed after next summer."

Crissy thought of that now as she walked through the rambling buildings. She always liked to tour the shop and put the carriages together in her mind as well as she could. She usually started with the blacksmith shop because she loved the smell of burning hickory which lingered about the place even after the smiths had put out their fires and gone home. Besides, the blacksmith shop was where the smiths said all the carriages got their start, anyway.

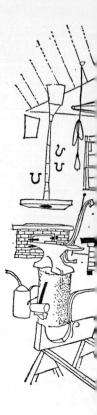

"Just like the foundation for a house," said Old Man Douglas, who was the oldest smith in the shop and therefore a sort of foreman. "Who puts the gear together so's the body'll have something to ride on, I'd like to know? Why, us smiths, and nobody else."

Crissy understood pretty well about the gear. It started out with the axle, which was in two pieces to begin with and had to be welded together. Then for a four-wheeled

vehicle, two axles were hitched together by a center piece,
and the springs were fastened on top, after which the
kingpin and a thing called the fifth wheel, which let the
carriage turn, were joined to the front axle.

"All that's a gear, and you can't get anywhere without
it," Old Man Douglas said huffily, "in spite of all the airs

Santa Clara County Free Library
San Jose, Calif.

those painters put on. Just window trimming, paint is. Surrey'd run just as well without any paint at all."

Papa said that Old Man Douglas's feud with the painters had been going on for years now and that everybody would be disappointed if he made peace with them. The other smiths, busy making lamp brackets, step irons and other small items, kept the shop ringing with the sound of their hammers on the anvils, each one of which, Old Man Douglas said, had a different sound once you got to listening for it.

The best part of the smith shop, though, Crissy always thought, was when Old Man Douglas fitted the red-hot metal tires to the wooden wheels. The wood never quite caught fire, but the smoke soared in sweet-smelling wisps from the wheels or from the wooden bodies on which the hot metal parts were being fitted.

"Just the way Aunt Henrietta fits dresses on me," said Crissy, "only cooler and with pins instead of a hammer."

"Crissy?" Papa's voice came to her from the depths of the auto shop. "You all right?"

"Oh, yes," called Crissy. "Just making a few carriages."

"Better make automobiles instead," said Papa, "and help your poor father."

A loud snort came from Mr. Wellfleet's balcony, and Crissy fled into the wood shop, where she hardly ever went because Mr. Higgins, who ran the shop, was so deaf that he always had to roar to make himself hear what he was saying. Since Crissy was not able to roar back quite loud enough, their conversations were never very satisfactory. Besides, the wood shop looked a good deal like a carpenter's shop and so was not so interesting as the trim and paint shops.

If it weren't for wanting to be loyal to Jed Haley, Crissy would almost have liked the trim shop the best of all. Here she could almost always find scraps of carpet or leather or whipcord for her doll house, which Papa had painted to look like the front of their own house. Crissy looked in the scrap box now to see if Mr. Harper, the trimmer, might have left a piece of something for her, but the box was empty except for little snippets that were of no use to anybody, even Crissy.

"Crissy!" called Papa. "We can go now."

Crissy skipped regretfully past the huge paint shop. She loved to look at the bright paints which made the carriages so handsome. They were all described in the catalog which Papa carried around to show the dealers. Red, dark green, primrose yellow, carmine, dark blue—buckets of paint in every color were sitting in the paint shop waiting to make the Wellfleet line the most beautiful in the country.

The first part of the paint job was never very interesting —just putty for the nail holes, a coat of yellow ocher, and several coats of something that looked very much like runny mud. Only after all this had been applied and rubbed down with pumice and water did the color coats go on and then the varnish, with more rubbing in between with pumice and water.

"And of course Jed Haley's stripes," Crissy murmured as she climbed into the automobile beside Papa.

It was complicated, all right, and the painting, especially, took weeks and weeks, with all the drying and rubbing down and repainting, but Crissy decided it was worth all the trouble to see a shining carriage go smartly down the street with the Wellfleet name on it.

The automobile looked as spruce as any of the carriages, though, Crissy thought as she sat proudly beside Papa. He had ordered this one painted a handsome dark green, with touches of red to set it off. The lamps were brass, to make it look even gayer, and Papa kept the whole thing dusted and polished until it shone.

"Can't sell anything that's any less than perfect," he said. "I like to be proud—makes me talk better."

Plenty of people stared after them as they whirled down the length of River Street. It was longer that way, but on a Saturday afternoon practically everybody in the county would get a look at the Wellfleet and, Papa hoped, want one just like it.

"They'd look at a monkey, too, though," Crissy told Papa, "and not want to buy one." A sudden thought struck her. "I know how it can be. Somebody can steal the Thanksgiving turkey and run away with it, but the policeman can catch him in an automobile and bring the turkey back again in time for dinner."

Papa looked baffled.

"It sounds unlikely," he said mildly, "but maybe if I knew what you were talking about—"

"The Thanksgiving play," said Crissy, "with the automobile in it. I thought it would be exciting, besides being good advertising. Do you think we could manage?"

"To get it on the school stage?" asked Papa. "I guess so. They had a horse on that stage once, and he didn't break through. We could lay a few planks to get up the steps on."

That was one of the nice things about Papa. He never thought things were impossible, the way Aunt Henrietta did. Papa always started out with an open mind and kept it open as long as possible, even if it was quite a lot of trouble.

"I guess this might be it," said Papa doubtfully, turning the Wellfleet into a narrow road that wound through the thick pine woods. "Must have been an Indian trail once."

In spite of knowing better, Crissy could not help a quivery feeling that perhaps there might be a couple of Indians left over to lurk among the pines. There was something scary about the sudden woodsy dimness after the bright sunshine outside the Pinery. She was glad that she had Papa with her to chase away any skulking she-didn't-know-whats that might be hiding in the shadows.

"Stop, Papa!" cried Crissy. "There isn't any more road!"

"Jed said there wouldn't be," said Papa. "We'll have to leave the automobile and walk the rest of the way."

Crissy hated to leave the beautiful green Wellfleet sitting alone in the wilderness, but she followed Papa obediently until he found an almost-hidden path winding even farther into the forest.

"You could get lost in here," said Crissy, "and nobody'd find you for days and days."

Papa grinned and pointed from a little open space.

"See that? It's the smokestack down at the waterworks."

Sure enough, the tip of the stack, which was the tallest thing in town, was just visible above the trees on the other side of the little valley.

"And the Pinery's all in the city limits, too," said Papa.

"It still looks wild," said Crissy, who was feeling much more secure now, "but I guess if Jed— Oh, Papa! Look!"

They had come to the edge of the knoll and were looking down at a little lake brown with the leaves which had fallen from the trees that edged its bank. Facing them across the lake was a building that looked very much like the picture of Shakespeare's home that Crissy had seen in Aunt Henrietta's set of Stoddard's *Lectures*.

"Isn't it pretty?" Crissy looked with interest at the three pointed gables and the second-story bay window. "I like the way the boards make a design on the white, too."

"Half-timbered, they call it," Papa explained. "They make a frame out of timbers and fill in the spaces with plaster."

"I like it, even if it does seem far away from everything," said Crissy, still thinking of possible Indians.

" 'O sacred solitude! divine retreat!' " Jed Haley appeared suddenly around a turn in the path. "(Somebody Young, born a long time ago and presumably now dead.) Step inside, friends, and enjoy the food for the soul that I spoke of."

They entered through a heavy wooden door, with a huge key in the lock. Jed stood back and let them get their first look inside. They were standing in an enormous room with plain whitewashed walls and a huge fireplace occupying almost one whole end. Windows with tiny leaded panes let in the afternoon sunlight.

"It *is* Shakespeare's house, isn't it?" Crissy asked.

"Only on the outside," said Jed. "The inside is entirely different, because it has to be a house and something else besides." His voice rang with pride as he turned Crissy around to face the opposite end of the room. "See that?"

Occupying the whole end of the room was a little six-sided structure that looked just as English as the house which contained it.

"It's a—" Crissy began doubtfully. "A theater?"

"The Globe," said Jed. "An exact replica of Shakespeare's theater, although much smaller, for a reason which I'll reveal later. Walk inside and look it over."

Crissy went through the doorway into a little room which had a miniature stage at one end, an open space in front of it, and little galleries on three sides.

"The common people stand in the pit," Jed explained. "That's the open space here in front of the stage. Then the gentry sit in the galleries, and there are special seats on the stage for the notables."

"Oh, my, I do wish Aunt Henrietta could hear him," thought Crissy.

It was strange to look at Jed, complete as usual with derby hat and cigar, and to hear him talking as though a lot of people from Shakespeare's time would come walking into his theater at any moment.

"But how did you ever—" Papa began.

"With these two hands, mostly." Jed held them out. "It took time to get the details just right, and all the money I could save, but it was worth it. I was in England once."

Crissy was busy trying to see everything at once, but she was not too busy to notice that Jed spoke almost with reverence, as though he were in church.

"One dream that came true," he said quietly, "because I made it come true. Lots of them didn't."

Crissy wondered then if Jed might have wanted to be a poet sometime, like the famous men whose words he was always quoting. Instead, he had had to build something with his hands.

"It's just beautiful," Crissy told him earnestly.

" 'A thing of beauty is a joy forever,' " said Jed. "(John Keats, born 1795, died 1821.) Now, if you will be seated, I have entertainment for you."

He pulled out a low wooden bench just big enough for Papa and Crissy to sit on side by side and disappeared behind the stage. Suddenly a fairylike figure appeared on the stage and began to sing in a high voice.

"A marionette!" cried Crissy. "Oh, Papa, just see!"

" 'Where the bee sucks, there suck I.

     · [sang the puppet]

     In a cowslip's bell I lie;

     There I couch when owls do cry.

     On the bat's back I do fly

     After summer merrily.

Merrily, merrily shall I live now

Under the blossom that hangs on the bough.' "

"Ariel," said Jed's voice offstage, "from *The Tempest*."

More characters from Shakespeare's plays appeared one by one or sometimes two by two on Jed's stage and spoke their lines while Crissy stared in fascination. Poetry rolled over her in waves of words as Jed made her laugh with Shakespeare's clowns or sigh with his beautiful heroines. Finally the last puppet went off the stage, and Jed emerged, rubbing stiff fingers.

"Remarkable!" said Papa. "Really remarkable!"

"I don't see how you do it!" cried Crissy. "I don't see how you fix the puppets or make them walk or say the words or—or anything!"

Jed re-lit his cigar and pushed his derby back on his head.

"It's a certain amount of trouble," he admitted, "or it

would be trouble if I didn't like to do it, which is the way with most things."

"I guess so," Crissy agreed. "May I look around outside, too?"

"Anywhere," said Jed. "Don't overlook the doghouse." He stuck his head out the back door and called. "Falstaff! Show the young lady your house!"

A fat white bulldog with an undershot jaw and a waddling gait emerged from a miniature house which looked exactly like the big house, even to the half-timbered front. Crissy ran to him and was enthusiastically licked by a lolling pink tongue. Falstaff squeezed through the doorway of his house and lay down inside, sticking his head out again as though to show Crissy how comfortable he was.

"You probably bark only Shakespeare-talk," Crissy told him, but Falstaff declined to say a single word.

"Time to go," Papa said finally. "Gets dark early in these woods, and I don't have the Wellfleet trained yet to find its way home."

"Peg could," said Crissy.

"So she could," Papa agreed, "though I don't think you should mention it, now that we're in the automobile business. Jed, we're really impressed with your place here. It's a work of art, no less."

"Come any time," said Jed, who had walked back with them to the automobile, "but don't be talking about it around town. I don't want a lot of cackling women cluttering up the place—only my friends."

"We're proud to be called that," said Papa with dignity. "Climb in, Crissy."

Just as Papa got the motor running, Jed reached into his pocket and handed Crissy the biggest lapel button she had ever seen.

"Souvenir," he said. "Maybe you collect 'em."

The button was at least five inches across and had a colored picture of an Indian on it.

"Got it at the Exposition in Buffalo last year," Jed yelled.

"It certainly is a beauty," called Crissy. "Thank you very much."

She waved, and the Wellfleet plunged down the narrow trail again.

"Just wait until Elmo sees that button!" said Crissy. "He'll die of envy. Why, I can make him do almost anything I say, just to get that Indian pin away from me. Papa, the automobile seems queer, doesn't it?"

"After Shakespeare, you mean? Yes, it does. In fact, I feel as though we should be riding away in one of those litters—"

"Those chairs on handles? I think so, too, except that we could walk just as fast."

Their feeling of belonging in another age vanished only when they had left the Pinery behind and were heading across the Flats toward home. Crissy looked back at the towering pines rising behind them.

"Papa, it was lots better than that entertainment at the Opera House last winter," she said, "and that man got paid."

"Jed's good, all right," Papa agreed. "If he could be persuaded to come out of those woods, he could make Granite City sit up and take notice. Maybe even some other places, too."

Halfway up the last hill, Dr. Agnew was twirling the crank of his stalled automobile. Papa pulled up behind him and climbed out. Dr. Agnew looked yearningly at his case of surgical instruments.

"I suppose not," he said, "though there's one article in there that would likely do the trick."

"The patients might not feel so secure if they knew it," Papa advised. "What about a screw driver instead?"

"Screw driver?" roared the doctor. "I've tried three of them, also a file, a pair of pliers, and some miscellaneous things, including nail clippers. Cassius!" He looked all around, but this time Rex and Cassius were not in sight. "Great day! I forgot he had to take Rex to be shod."

"Ride with us," said Papa. "Crissy can sit on your lap, if you don't mind."

"I hate to crowd you," said Dr. Agnew, "but I have a patient that needs me. Just let me get my medicine case."

Crissy was happy that the Wellfleet started off so briskly, even though she did feel rather large and conspicuous sitting on the doctor's lap.

"I'll find Cassius at the smith's and tell him to come for you," Papa said as he dropped the doctor at his patient's house, "and leave word for them to haul your machine in, too."

"And for the last time!" said the doctor curtly. "Enough's enough. I want a Wellfleet waiting at my front door the first thing Monday morning."

"It'll be there," said Papa without turning a hair, although Crissy was ready to explode with excitement. "Any particular color?"

"No, no, just so it runs."

The doctor vanished behind his patient's front door.

"Papa!" cried Crissy. "You sold one—and you weren't even trying!"

"The first of many," said Papa calmly. "And truth compels me to state that I saw the doctor driving out that way while we were at the Pinery—or heard him, rather." Papa gave a triumphant little chuckle. "I thought the motor sounded unusually bad."

5

TURKEY FOR CHRISTMAS

Crissy crawled out of bed and, for the first time in her life, was sorry to see snow.

"But only because of the automobiles," she told Susan-Cat, who, strictly against Aunt Henrietta's rules, had spent the night on the foot of Crissy's bed.

"Snow and automobiles just don't go together," Papa had admitted to Crissy, although he was careful not to make such a statement in front of anybody who might be a prospective customer. "At least they don't yet. Sometime, though, you'll see automobiles on the roads no matter what the weather is."

Crissy wouldn't have believed it if anybody but Papa had said so, and she knew that most people probably wouldn't believe it anyway because of the automobile being something new and untried. In the meantime, horses were going to be the thing during the snowy weather.

"And I do wish it had held off just a little longer," thought Crissy.

Of course it had held off longer than usual already, but that had been no help at all, because people just said, "No sense in thinking about an automobile now. Going to snow any day. Come around next spring, and we'll see."

Spring looked a long way off to Crissy just now, as she scrambled into her wool school dress in the cold bedroom and rushed downstairs to warm up beside the kitchen stove. There would be no fire in the base burner in the dining room until dinner time, because nobody had time to build a fire in more than one place before breakfast, and of course that one place had to be the kitchen stove, which cooked as well as heated.

"Don't hump over," said Aunt Henrietta as Crissy stirred her oatmeal around and around with her spoon and stared disconsolately at the snowy landscape. "Sit up straight or you'll never look like anything. Martha May has such nice posture."

"Pooh to Martha May," thought Crissy, being careful not to say it out loud. "Who wants to be like Martha May, anyway?"

Martha May didn't have a papa who sold automobiles. Probably Martha May had never even ridden in an automobile, a fact which made Crissy feel so superior that she almost forgave Martha May her golden hair and her equally golden manners. Papa winked at Crissy as though he knew what she was thinking.

"Too bad it's only the first snow," he said. "We'd get the sleigh out."

"I'm glad it *is* the first snow. It would have spoiled the Thanksgiving play if it had come any sooner."

"I certainly couldn't have driven the machine over to the school in snow," Papa agreed.

Crissy was very much pleased with the way the play had come out. Papa had obligingly driven the Wellfleet across the stage, not once but twice, returning triumphantly the second time with the make-believe turkey which had been stolen from the poor family in the play.

Crissy was proud that it was the first time an automobile had appeared on any stage in Granite City or probably anywhere else except New York or Paris. She had been certain from the loud applause as the Wellfleet chugged across the stage that people would be flocking down the very next morning to buy automobiles from Papa. Why, maybe he might not even have enough to supply the demand. Instead, nobody had come at all, and the four machines which Mr. Wellfleet had finished after Dr. Agnew's were sitting down at the Works, where Crissy supposed they would spend the rest of the winter in peace and quiet.

On the way to school, Crissy automatically scuffed through the snow so that it sprayed up over her high buttoned shoes, but the snow just wasn't as much fun as usual, even though every fence post had a peaked cap of white and every gust of wind blew showers of snow from the laden branches.

"It's not wet enough to pack yet," said Elmo, who was paddling along behind her, kicking through the drifts like a snow plow. "Maybe by the time school's out and the sun gets a chance at it— Hey, is your father going to race Peg on New Year's?"

Crissy brightened a little then.

"He hasn't said, but he always does."

The races on New Year's afternoon the length of River Street were always fun. Anybody in town who thought he had a good fast horse got a chance to prove it on that day if the snow packed right for racing. Crissy never knew whether it was more fun to stand on the sidelines and watch the graceful sleighs whirl by or to ride wrapped up in the bearskin robe beside Papa while Peg stepped off the blocks.

"I guess I'd rather ride this year," she decided, "if Aunt Henrietta will let me."

Last year Aunt Henrietta had felt that it would have been better for Crissy to watch instead of ride, but that was mostly because Martha May and Mrs. Garrett had watched, attired in their Christmas finery and looking, Crissy thought, much too elaborately dressed for a horse race. She supposed that Aunt Henrietta would try to keep Crissy away entirely if she knew about the bets that some of the men usually put on their favorite horses.

"I don't know if I'll go or not," said Elmo with an air of unconcern. "Same old thing every year."

Crissy immediately decided to ask Papa if Elmo could

ride in the race with them. Elmo's father didn't even have
a horse, which Crissy considered a great pity, and Elmo was
rather sensitive about it, always pretending that he didn't
like horses or would rather have a bicycle or any reason at
all. All the same, he spent hours with Peg in the barn and
always looked wistful whenever he saw Peg and the rig
going by. Besides, Elmo was lonesome just now because he
had sold all his rabbits to somebody who had a warm place
to keep them during the cold weather.

While she was asking, Crissy guessed she would start
suggesting to Papa that she was planning on riding with
him in a Wellfleet in the Diamond Jubilee parade. Aunt
Henrietta probably wouldn't like that, either, but if Papa
decided this early that Crissy could do it Aunt Henrietta
would have time to get used to the idea by next summer.
Crissy had another wonderful idea about the parade, too,
but she decided to save that one until later. Maybe she
might not even get her courage up to mention it at all, but
it was nice to think about, anyway.

Crissy rushed home after school and went upstairs to
take a few stitches on the embroidered towel which she was
making for Aunt Henrietta for Christmas.

"I do hate to embroider," she told Susan-Cat, "even
worse than washing dishes."

The only reason she was making the towel was because
Aunt Henrietta was always talking about what beautiful

embroidery Martha May did. Already Crissy's piece looked
rather smudged, but she kept at it, ripping out and redoing
every bit that wasn't exactly right. She was glad when it
was time to go off to school and forget about embroidery
for a while. She wasn't planning any such nonsense for
Papa, for whom she had saved up her allowance to buy
a pair of heavy leather gloves with wide, flaring cuffs for
driving Wellfleets in chilly weather.

Christmas was going to be especially much fun this
year, because Mr. Wellfleet had asked Crissy to help pass
out the Christmas turkeys which he gave to all his men
each year, along with bags of candy for those who had children. Crissy didn't especially care about dead turkeys, but
fortunately they had legs for handles that she could hang
on by.

"Never saw any given away except with the legs on,"
said Papa when Crissy had questioned him on this point,
"so I wouldn't worry. Maybe he'll have you pass out the
candy instead."

"Oh, I hope not," said Crissy, who thought that turkeys,
even raw, were much more interesting than bags of candy.
"I can always pretend they're already roasted and sitting
on a platter with the stuffing popping out."

There seemed to be much more to do this Christmas
than any other Christmas that Crissy could remember. As
usual, she was in the school exercises, but this time only

to speak a piece. She was also in the Sunday School program, which meant that she had to go down to the church after supper two or three nights a week and wait patiently to say the two lines which she had in the Christmas pageant. She was going to be a shepherd, in Papa's old bathrobe with a towel around her head and a crook in her hand. Martha May, as usual, would be an angel and, to make it especially realistic, Mrs. Garrett had offered to have her husband rig up a pulley so that Martha May could be suspended over the platform.

"I hope her halo falls off," muttered Elmo, who was going to be a shepherd, too, "or maybe the rope might break."

A thoughtful look came across his face.

"I've got a pretty good jackknife," he remarked.

"Don't you dare!" said Crissy. "Everybody knew you were going to push her into that tub at Halloween, and you'll be blamed if anything happens to her and you're within five miles."

"I guess so," said Elmo regretfully, "but it does seem—"

"Besides, Christmas is different," Crissy argued. "We wouldn't want to play tricks at Christmas."

"N-no," said Elmo, "we wouldn't, but it's nice to pretend we would."

The week before Christmas was a real whirl, with final

rehearsals for everything and more snow falling every day or so and the Christmas tree to be hunted at the Pinery.

"If it's like this, it'll be wonderful for the race," Crissy told Papa as they trudged through the deep snow to find a very special little spruce tree which Jed Haley had recommended.

" 'O Christmas tree, O Christmas tree, How lovely are your branches!' " Jed had said. "(German folk song, nobody knows when.) This tree has the loveliest branches you ever saw, and it's just the right size, besides."

Crissy and Papa had no trouble finding the tree, because Jed had tied a red ribbon on its topknot like a hair ribbon so that it stood out from all the other trees along the path to his house. The house looked very picturesque, Crissy thought, with snow all around it and the evergreens dark against the cold, gray sky. Falstaff came out of his dog-house, woofed at them once, wagged his corkscrew tail, and crawled back inside. Jed, much to Crissy's disappointment, was at work.

"Where I would be, too," said Papa, "if I were selling carriages instead of automobiles."

For a minute, Crissy wondered if Papa might be sorry he had gone into the automobile business.

"Papa," she began, "maybe you should—"

"No, I shouldn't," said Papa in a hearty voice. "There are problems, all right, like people who think that machines made somewhere else are better than the ones we make right here in Granite City—which they're not—but there's not a thing that we can't work out. It just takes time and a lot of talking." Papa put on his most determined expression. "Just remember, young lady, we're in the automobile business to stay."

Crissy wished she could feel as positive as Papa sounded. She was tired of people who asked how he was getting along and then put on an I-doubt-it look when Crissy said he was doing just fine.

"But Papa *says* he's doing just fine," Crissy argued to herself, "and he certainly ought to know."

But still she wished rather uneasily that Papa would sell carriages at the same time as automobiles. She should think he could do both, even though he had explained to Mr. Wellfleet that he didn't feel he could work conscientiously at two things at once, especially as selling automobiles was much harder work than selling carriages, which everybody was used to, anyway.

"I suppose if he can't, he can't," Crissy told herself, feeling rather disloyal, "but I do wish he could."

"Here, we'll untie the ribbon." Papa swung his ax at the base of the little Christmas tree. "You might want it for a souvenir."

They dragged the tree back along the path to where Peg and the sleigh were waiting. Peg whinnied at sight of them, and Crissy gave her the crunchy apple which she had brought along for a special treat.

"I like horses," said Crissy, "especially Peg. We'll always keep her, won't we?"

"Of course." Papa slapped the reins against Peg's back, and they spun along the snowy road. "Peg's a member of the family, just like Susan-Cat."

"And me," said Crissy contentedly.

"You?" Papa grinned at her. "Who said anything about keeping you forever? You'll probably grow up and get so big the house won't hold you, or you'll take a notion to dye your hair orange, which won't go with Hen's color scheme, or—"

Crissy squeezed his hand hard, repenting already of having had any doubts at all about anything he might do, whether it concerned automobiles or even flying through the air, crazy as that sounded.

The Christmas tree stood on the back porch for a few days while Crissy strung cranberries and popcorn to help decorate it and while Aunt Henrietta rummaged in the attic to find the box of candles and the little clips that held them to the branches. Best of all, she brought down the Christmas angel, with her golden wings and her star-spangled white dress, for Crissy to fasten on the very top of the tree.

The morning before Christmas, Crissy hurried into her

second-best dress and started out for the Carriage Works. Papa had gone earlier with Peg and the sleigh, but Mr. Wellfleet wouldn't need Crissy until eleven o'clock, when the turkeys would be given out and the plant closed for the afternoon. Crissy noted with satisfaction that the snow was packed hard on the streets, with loose snow only along the edges where people drove their rigs just when they had to pass. She supposed that on River Street it would be packed all the way across, because everybody traveling that way would try to make the New Year's racetrack as smooth as possible.

"If it will only stay good and cold for another week!" Crissy thought. "A thaw would spoil everything."

Elmo came tearing out of his house with his skates over his shoulder and walked with Crissy as far as the Branch, which was frozen over just right for skating. Somebody had brought a snow shovel, and the usual swarm of boys took turns pushing the blown snow back to make a clear space where the ice was the smoothest.

"Don't you wish you were coming?" yelled Elmo, spying the rest of the skaters and rushing across the ice toward them. "Too bad you're only a girl!"

For a minute, Crissy felt wounded, but then she remembered that Elmo was probably just jealous because she was going down to the Works to help give out the turkeys. Elmo's father had a nice job at the bank, but that wasn't nearly as interesting a place to go as the Carriage Works, especially now that Mr. Wellfleet was making automobiles as well as carriages.

"Besides, maybe Papa'll take me skating some night after supper," she thought.

In spite of an unhappy tendency of her ankles to turn over, Crissy loved to go skating, especially at night. Papa always crossed hands with her and helped her keep her balance, so that she felt as though she were skating just as well as anybody else. The stars always seemed to be hanging especially high on such nights, and even people who were rather ordinary in the daytime looked handsome and mysterious as they glided by in the starlight.

Crissy was thinking so hard about skating that she walked almost all the way past the Works before Jed Haley managed to rush out and stop her.

" 'We weep to see you haste away so soon,' " he said. "(Robert Herrick, born 1591, died 1674.) Especially when you haven't been here yet. Step inside. It's five after eleven, and Mr. Wellfleet's champing at the bit."

Crissy scurried into the Works. A red farm wagon had been pulled in front of the door, and in the wagon were two huge washtubs filled with dead turkeys and two bushel baskets filled with fat sacks of Christmas candy. Tethered to the wagon wheel were two live turkeys, which, according to Mr. Wellfleet's usual custom, went to the bachelors in the plant.

"Fatten 'em up until you get wives to cook 'em for you," he always advised heartily.

Mr. Wellfleet was stamping impatiently up and down, looking at his watch.

"Here you are!" he said before Crissy even got her coat off. "Let's begin. May as well have it over with."

Papa winked at Crissy, so that she knew that Mr. Wellfleet was acting huffy because he felt embarrassed about giving presents.

"Makes me look as though I thought I was better than they are," he sometimes sputtered. "Here-my-good-man sort of thing. Why, those men of mine are the best workmen in Granite City, and nobody has to give them anything."

Every year, though, the turkeys and candy appeared just as usual.

"Christmas spirit always gets me at the last minute," Mr. Wellfleet told Papa sheepishly. "Can't seem to help myself."

The men swarmed out of all the different shops, putting on their outside coats as they came. Everybody knew that there was no nonsense about Mr. Wellfleet. He gave out the turkeys, yelled "Merry Christmas," and expected everybody to go home right then.

"Up with you, young lady." Mr. Wellfleet boosted Crissy into the wagon box. "You stand right there and give everybody a turkey when they walk past." He clapped his hands for attention. "All right, men! Right this way. Miss Crissy has something for you all. And we wish you a Merry Christmas, don't we, Crissy? Here, I'll hand out the candy."

Although Mr. Wellfleet pretended that he was all business, he knew exactly which men had children, how many of each, and what their names were. He loved to hand out the right number of bags of candy and to ask about the children by name.

Crissy grabbed the first turkey firmly by the legs and gave it to the foreman of the paint shop.

"Why, it isn't so bad at all!" she exclaimed. "Their legs don't even feel raw—just sort of scaly—and the feathers help a lot, too!"

After that, it was all fun—the Merry Christmases from every direction and the turkeys being handed out to Old Man Douglas from the smith shop, deaf Mr. Higgins from the wood shop, Mr. Harper the trimmer, half a dozen painters, a few apprentices, a dozen more men from the different departments, and, last of all, the two bachelors, Jed Haley and young Sim Lathrop from the smith shop, to whom Mr. Wellfleet presented the live turkeys with a flourish.

"And an ear of corn apiece, too," he announced, "to help out on the feed bill."

Icy air rushed through the door as each man called out "Merry Christmas" and went out with his turkey.

"That wasn't hard," said Crissy when the last turkey was gone and Mr. Wellfleet's baskets of candy were empty. "My goodness, what's that awful noise?"

From outside came yells, howls, roars of laughter, and voices raised in argument. Crissy climbed down out of the wagon and rushed to the door.

"Oh!" she cried. "Oh, dear, they're arguing again!"

As usual, the smith shop and the paint shop were wrangling, with Old Man Douglas heading the smiths, and a big burly Irishman named Grogarty speaking for the paint shop.

"Blacksmiths, is it?" howled Grogarty. "And who'd be buying a carriage with no paint on it?"

"Paint!" Old Man Douglas yelled back. "Can paint hold a carriage together, you black-hearted villain? Why, even Sim's turkey knows better than that."

"We'll see how much he knows!" yelled Grogarty. "About as much as the smiths, most likely. Jed, let's have that turkey of yours! And the corn, too, as soon as you get it shelled."

Everybody crowded around Grogarty, and Crissy managed to wriggle her way into the front row.

"Now then, we'll just let these two turkeys decide who's better—the smiths or the painters," Grogarty roared. "We'll drop the corn in two rows, like this, and the turkey that gets to the end of his row first is the winner. If it's Jed's turkey, which it's bound to be, there'll be no more gab from you smiths about how important you are. Ah, that'll be a peaceful day!"

"It's a day you'll never see!" shouted Old Man Douglas. "Any idiot can tell that Sim's turkey is a superior bird, a winner if ever I saw one. It'll be us smiths that'll be working in peace, with no foolish clacking in our ears. Come on, are you afraid to let 'em go?"

Sim and Jed started their turkeys off both at once, and each bird began gobbling corn ahead of himself.

"There!" yelled Grogarty. "What'd I tell you? Ours is winning!"

"What! Yours is a mile behind!" retorted Old Man Douglas. "Hey! They can't do that!"

Suddenly the turkeys spied each other's supply of corn and began dashing back and forth from one row to the other until nobody could tell which one belonged where or which bird was which. The turkeys gobbled angrily and began chasing each other through the snow, pecking and quarreling. A few turkey feathers floated through the air as the birds took off across the vacant lot, with Jed and young Sim in close pursuit. Mrs. Grogarty, a tiny woman with bright red hair, came trotting up the street with her market basket full of groceries.

"Grogarty!" she shrieked. "What kind of tomfoolery is this? Is that our turkey that's wearing all the fat off his frame flapping around the countryside like that?"

"No, Mary," said Grogarty meekly. "Ours is that dead one keeping cool in the snowdrift."

"Killed in a fight, no doubt! Well, get him out of the snowdrift and come along," Mrs. Grogarty ordered. "Next time you'll lose him entirely, and there'll be no Christmas dinner for Grogarty."

Grogarty meekly took the market basket and followed his wife along the snowy street. He looked wistfully back.

"Merry Christmas to you all—even the smiths," he called. "And the painters would have won fair and square if only those stupid birds had kept their wits about them!"

"One excuse is as good as the next," Old Man Douglas retorted. "But a Merry Christmas to you, anyway, and we'll go into the subject further at another time."

"Now they'll keep on arguing worse than ever," Crissy told Papa as they were riding home in the sleigh behind Peg.

"Keeps 'em happy," said Papa cheerfully, "which is what you want in this life."

Dinner was on the table when Crissy and Papa came in, sweeping the snow off their feet with the broom which Aunt Henrietta kept on the back porch for the purpose. The house smelled deliciously of Christmas—pine needles and fruit cake and ginger cookies and mince pie.

The portieres into the parlor were tightly drawn, but Crissy knew that the tree was waiting in shining beauty in the bay window, with a bucket of water standing handy in case of fire. Aunt Henrietta had done quite a lot of fussing about the candles on the tree, making sure that each one was clipped on so that it could not possibly set fire to the branch above.

"I do wish there were some other way to light a tree," she worried as Crissy hurried into the parlor just after supper with the last of the presents which she had been wrapping all afternoon. "Sometimes I think we shouldn't have any candles. Hurry now, Clarissa Jane, or we'll be late for the program."

Crissy wriggled into the new red wool dress which Aunt Henrietta had made her especially for tonight's Christmas Eve program at the church. The new dress wouldn't make any difference at the pageant, because it would be under Papa's bathrobe, but it would look wonderful when Crissy walked up the aisle as her name was called for the present-giving. Afterward, the tree at home would be lighted and Crissy would open every one of her presents, even if it meant staying up as late as eleven o'clock.

Crissy screwed up her face as Aunt Henrietta undid the kid curlers which had held her hair in horrid little knots all afternoon. On Christmas, Aunt Henrietta insisted, Crissy was going to have curls like everybody else.

"Like Martha May," Crissy grumbled to herself as Aunt Henrietta ran the comb through the corkscrews which emerged from the curlers. "I do get tired of Martha May."

She had to admit, though, when Aunt Henrietta had brushed the hair around her finger into long curls and tied a red ribbon on top, that she looked rather better than usual—"which shouldn't be hard," Crissy told herself impatiently, "with no place to go but up." Aunt Henrietta had been doubtful about the red dress, but now she nodded her head in approval.

"Very good," she said. "I think you'll turn out to be the striking type, so we may as well begin early."

Crissy knew that Aunt Henrietta preferred the angelic type like Martha May, but it was going to be a lot more comfortable if she would reconcile herself to Crissy being like Crissy and not like Martha May.

A light snow was falling when Papa and Aunt Henrietta and Crissy left for the church, and Crissy could feel her curls gradually straightening out, in spite of the woolen scarf which was wrapped around her head to keep out the dampness.

Crissy hurried to lay several presents under the big Christmas tree—a handkerchief for Martha May, notepaper for the Sunday School teacher, and the Indian lapel pin for Elmo. Crissy felt very noble about giving up the Indian pin when it would have been so useful for getting Elmo to do something important that she might want done in the future. Still, Elmo was a good friend, and she knew that nothing else would please him half as much as that Indian pin.

"I got a muff for Christmas," Martha May announced to Crissy. "Mama gave it to me early so I could carry it to-night, but she's holding it for me until after the pageant. I thought I'd carry it when I go up for my presents."

"Place seems warm enough to me," said Elmo. "No need for either muffs or mittens."

"How can anybody see it—" Martha May objected, but just then the choir leader beckoned to her.

Complete with halo, wings and a flowing white dress, she was hoisted aloft on her pulley, where, Crissy admitted, she looked very angelic indeed. The whole pageant was a great success, Crissy thought, in spite of Elmo's hopeful glances toward the pulley, which remained disappointingly steady.

At last the pageant was over, the curtains were pulled, and the Sunday School superintendent began calling the names for the Christmas presents. Everybody had at least a bag of candy and a small gift, and a few children trotted up the aisle several times for extra presents from their friends.

"Jimmy Bates," said the superintendent. "Sarah Jane Dobbs. Martha May Garrett." Silence. "Martha May Garrett?"

"I'm up here," said a muffled voice behind the curtains. "Papa got the ropes mixed up, and he can't find the right one to let me down."

The superintendent and the minister vanished behind the curtains to help Mr. Garrett get his child down from her angelic perch, and the audience buzzed excitedly. Crissy caught Elmo's delighted gaze across the church and knew that the evening had been much improved for him.

"And it wasn't anything he did, either," she thought, "which makes it ever so much nicer, like the cider on her hair."

As Martha May, breathless and red-faced, darted back

to get her muff from her mother before marching up for
her presents, Crissy heard Aunt Henrietta give an exasper-
ated sniff.

"You'd think," she muttered to Crissy, "that she was
the only child that ever had a muff. It's all I've heard for
weeks from Mrs. Garrett. I do declare—"

Crissy, astonished, tucked her hand into Aunt Henrietta's. It was nice, she thought, to find out that people
were thinking the same things that she was.

"Clarissa Jane Bingham!"

Crissy slid out of the pew and went up for her presents—
a pair of pink hair ribbons from Martha May, who knew
that Crissy hated pink, and, surprisingly, a bottle of violet
perfume from Elmo.

"Girls like the silliest stuff!" said Elmo, turning bright
red when Crissy waylaid him after the program to say
thank you. "Who wants to smell like a violet, anyway?"
He opened his coat and showed her the Indian pin fastened
to his shirt pocket along with others of his treasured collection. "It's a swell pin, but Mama won't let me wear it
on the outside in church. Lookit, though."

He grinned and pointed to a pin which said, "Thank
you. Come again," and then, even more blushingly, to a
second pin that announced, "There ain't no flies on you."

"Gotta be getting home," he muttered hastily and fled,
forgetting to close the door behind him.

The tree at home was beautiful, twinkling with candles and gay with the strings of popcorn and cranberries, at which Susan-Cat kept nibbling.

"Hoping they'll taste like salmon, I suppose," said Papa.

"I do have a can of salmon for her," said Aunt Henrietta, "but she can't have it until Christmas dinner tomorrow."

Crissy had made a catnip mouse for Susan, who batted it happily across the carpet. Aunt Henrietta exclaimed over her towel, and Papa put on his new gauntlets and insisted that he was going to wear them until bedtime.

"Start on your own packages," Aunt Henrietta urged.

"Never know what you might find," said Papa. "Lions or tigers or kangaroos, even."

Crissy hoped not. Her first package, from Mr. Wellfleet, contained an iron paperweight shaped like a carriage. Her second, from Papa, held a pair of shiny new ice skates. Her third—

"Something squashy," said Crissy. "I— Why, it's a muff!"

The muff was made of soft tan rabbit fur, with a celluloid ring for Crissy to slide her hand through and a brown velvet lining.

"It's lovely!" cried Crissy. "Oh, Aunt Henrietta, I do thank you!" She buried her nose in the fur and sniffed the lovely soft smell. "I'll carry it for the New Year's race!"

"Just be sure," said Aunt Henrietta tartly, "that Martha May Garrett gets a good look at it!"

Even when she was tucked into her bed and her eyes felt as though they were filled with sand, Crissy tried to keep awake to think about all the things that had made the day so wonderful—the violet perfume, with which she had thoroughly doused her pillow; her curls, even though they had proved to be very temporary; the new muff, the ice skates, and, best of all, the turkey race.

"Except," she murmured sleepily, "that it didn't last nearly long enough!"

6

THE NEW YEAR'S RACE

"Waffles! Waffles and maple sirup!"

Aunt Henrietta's voice floated up the stairs to Crissy, who still lay burrowed under the covers on New Year's morning. It was much too early to get up, she thought, especially since she had been allowed to stay up the night before to see the New Year in. She still seemed to feel the cold air on her face as she had stood with Papa on the front porch to listen to the frosty sound of church bells, dinner bells, and shotguns as Granite City welcomed in the new year. The beginning of 1903, thought Crissy, had seemed much the same as the end of 1902, especially as she had hardly been able to keep her eyes open at the time.

"Waffles!"

Suddenly Crissy woke up enough to realize what Aunt Henrietta was saying. Always on New Year's morning, Aunt Henrietta got out the old black waffle iron and had waffles and real maple sirup for breakfast. It was apt to be all the food anybody would have until evening, except for a snack at noon on the kitchen table, because in the late afternoon practically everybody in town made their New Year's calls, going from house to house and sampling the collations which the ladies spread on their dining tables for all comers.

"I'm up!" called Crissy. "Shoo, Susan!"

She let Susan go downstairs ahead of her, although she supposed that by now Aunt Henrietta suspected that Susan slept on Crissy's bed almost every night.

It was going to be a wonderful day for the racing and for everything else, Crissy thought. The sun was shining but not enough to melt the snow, which would be pleasantly crunchy underfoot.

"A fine start for the New Year!" said Papa as they sat down to breakfast. "A beautiful day, a horse race ahead, and a collation at the end. And only nineteen automobiles to sell before the Fourth of July!" he ended ruefully.

Some days Crissy didn't think Papa could ever manage, but the sun was shining so brightly today that she couldn't possibly worry, even though Aunt Henrietta was showing signs of starting to. Crissy hastily began talking about something else.

"Do you want me to set the good dishes out on the dining table?" she asked. "And the cups and saucers?"

"If you'll be careful," said Aunt Henrietta absently. "I have the silver all polished and the jellied chicken keeping ice-cold on the back porch and the cakes all made, though I have to frost them still, and—"

Her voice trailed off, and Crissy knew that her thoughts had left them entirely and were probably fixed on such matters as hot biscuits and pots of coffee and how many cups for how many people.

"Maybe we could go skating," Crissy whispered to Papa, who shook his head.

"I don't think so. Hen will need us both to help get ready for the company, and I'll have to warm Peg up gradually for the race. She has to be curried, besides, and I want to touch up that place where the paint got scraped off the sleigh."

Crissy sighed. She did love to skate, and Papa had been taking her nearly every night, now that she had her new skates, which seemed to skate much better than the old ones had. Her ankles were stiffening up, and she even attempted a timid figure eight on the ice now and then when she was sure nobody was looking.

She opened the door to the china closet and set out Aunt Henrietta's hand-painted cups. Crissy admired them all— the one with the violets, the one with the roses, the one with the scarlet poppies—but her favorite was covered with pale blue forget-me-nots and had a little golden butterfly on the handle. She matched up the cups and saucers and arranged them on the big table, making sure that the forget-me-not one was in the front row where everybody would be sure to see it.

Dishes were nice to look at, she thought, because they always reminded her of all the special occasions when she had eaten off them. She smoothed down Aunt Henrietta's big Irish linen tablecloth with the hemstitched edges and the embroidered initial in the corner. The initial was "B" for Bingham, but Crissy thought she could see where it had once been "A" for Agnew and had been painfully picked out and done over.

"I wonder if the doctor will come to call today," thought Crissy. "He's a friend of Papa's, so I should think—"

She couldn't remember whether Dr. Agnew had come to the New Year's parties in other years. She probably wouldn't have noticed, anyway, because last year she had not known about his old romance with Aunt Henrietta. She stared after her aunt's brisk figure whisking through the house. It would be ever so much more fun for Aunt Henrietta, Crissy thought, if it were her own house instead of Papa's, but perhaps Aunt Henrietta didn't feel that way about it at all. It was very hard, Crissy thought, to know what grownups did think, because mostly it didn't show on the outside very much.

At noon there were delicious smells all through the kitchen, but none of them turned into anything more interesting than milk and cold beans for Crissy and Papa.

"Everything's practically ready," said Aunt Henrietta in satisfaction. "We can just come home from the race and set things out."

She sniffed the air and looked suspiciously at Papa. Papa pretended to cringe.

"I know I smell like a barn," he admitted, "but I've been currying Peg, and I haven't had time to change my clothes yet."

"See that you find time," said Aunt Henrietta dangerously. "What will everybody think if—"

"They'll think I've got a horse, same as they have," said Papa. "Don't worry, though. I'll be dressed to kill when the time comes."

Papa did look handsome when he and Crissy and Aunt Henrietta started out in the sleigh, with Peg stepping high in the frosty air. He was wearing his best suit and overcoat, with a derby hat like Jed Haley's, only in a less battered condition. Aunt Henrietta was wearing her brown velvet hat with the two ostrich plumes, and Crissy was carrying her Christmas muff. Even the bearskin robe, tucked carefully around Aunt Henrietta and Crissy, looked dressed up with its fluted edges and lining of red wool.

"Just let me out here, Andrew," said Aunt Henrietta when they reached the corner of River Street. "I see Mrs. Garrett and some others over there, and I'll stay with them." She smiled at Crissy. "Be sure your muff shows. I wouldn't want Martha May to miss it."

It was very exciting up at the starting line at the far end of River Street. There were at least a dozen horses—"accompanied," said Papa, "by their owners"—trying out the track until it was time for the race to begin. Papa took Peg down part of the course and brought her smartly back to the finish line.

"Elmo!" cried Crissy. "We forgot Elmo!"

"I told him to meet us here," said Papa. "Climb down and hunt him up for me. There's plenty of time."

Crissy didn't have long to hunt, because Elmo was already pushing through the crowd of men around the starting line.

"Here you are!" cried Crissy. "Papa says—"

"Shhhh!" Elmo gestured violently toward the back of

a chunky man who was talking to a group around him. "Just listen."

"There's Bingham!" the man said loudly. "Seems he'd be driving one of them new-fangled horseless carriages that he's so set on, instead of a horse and sleigh like us common folks."

"Can't drive automobiles on snow," somebody argued.

"Bah! Truth is, you can't drive automobiles on anything, and he knows it. Thinks that horse of his is something, too, but—"

Elmo and Crissy stepped briskly around in front of the speaker.

"Which horse do you fancy, sir?" Elmo asked in a polite voice.

"Wh— Why, my own, young man! Whose else? You young folks want to place a little bet, maybe?"

He guffawed loudly, but Elmo gave him a cold stare.

"Might," said Elmo.

"Peg is better than any other horse in town," said Crissy hotly, "and so are my father's automobiles better. My goodness, you probably never even rode in an automobile or you wouldn't be talking so silly."

"Well! A regular little spitfire!" said the fat man. "Listen, Sis! Everybody'll have forgotten all about automobiles by this time next year, so you might as well save your breath!"

"A lot you know!" Crissy was painfully aware that Aunt

Henrietta would not have approved of this—not the least bit in the world—but she couldn't seem to stop talking. "Why, I'll bet you—"

"What'll you bet? A nickel for candy, I suppose," the fat man sneered. "Or maybe that fancy muff? Just kid stuff!"

"Either put up or shut up!" said Jed Haley at Crissy's elbow. He eyed the fat man severely. "Just tell the young lady what you're figuring on betting. Or are you afraid to bet at all on that bag of bones you're driving?"

"Bag of bones! That horse! Why, he's the best racer in—" The fat man almost jumped up and down in his rage. "All right! I'll bet! Muffs, or what-have-you!"

Crissy, in whose ear Jed had been whispering urgently, stood up straight and looked the fat man in the eye.

"If your horse wins, you get my muff," she said. "If Peg wins, you go down and buy a horseless carriage from my father."

"Oh, now!" The fat man turned so red that Crissy wondered if maybe he might be going to explode. "There's no justice to that. A horseless carriage costs a lot of money."

"It's worth a lot of money, too," Elmo put in. "You'd be doing yourself a favor to get one."

"It's far and away too much to spend," sputtered the fat man. "Anyway, I was just fooling. Why, you're only a couple of kids."

But the men around him laughed him down.

"Afraid you'll lose?" they jeered.

"Kids are smarter dealers than you, even!"

"Want to keep your money forever?"

"Be a sport! It was you that started it!"

"You'll look good carrying that muff!"

The fat man looked around at the circle of faces and threw up his hands.

"All right, all right," he said sullenly. "I won't be losing, though."

He pushed his way through the crowd and was gone. Crissy stared after him in horror and hung on to her muff more tightly. Why, Aunt Henrietta would be simply wild if she lost the muff—and on a bet, besides. Jed Haley looked at her triumphantly.

"Very neat," he said. "If we can't sell machines one way, we can another, and that old windbag has money to burn."

"But just suppose—"

"Peg'll win," said Elmo confidently, "and think how your father will feel when he finds out we sold another automobile."

Crissy nodded, but she could feel her chin quivering a little as she climbed into the sleigh between Papa and Elmo. She immediately climbed down again and fed Peg the carrot which she had carried from home, wrapped up in her best handkerchief.

"Please, please do try to win," she whispered in Peg's ear. "It's very, very important!"

She climbed back into the sleigh and looked around for the fat man, who was driving a big rangy bay horse with eyes which rolled nervously at the crowd.

"Why, there's Jethro Blade!" Papa exclaimed at sight of the fat man. "He has a first-rate horse, though a fidgety one, especially when Jethro's driving. Well, here we go!"

The rigs all wheeled into place, and Mr. Wellfleet, who was the starter today, yelled "Go!" The bay horse reared, but started off at a smart clip just the same.

"All right, Peg," said Papa calmly. "Let's go!"

Crissy wished that she had had time to tell Papa how important it was for him to beat Jethro Blade's bay horse, but she was pretty sure she could depend on him to try to win. And of course Peg would do her very best, anyway, because if there was anything Peg loved it was a race. Maybe Papa knew that, too, and let her go her own way, so she wouldn't be distracted by any directions he might give her. Crissy watched admiringly as Papa guided Peg easily into a gap in the ranks of the racers. The bay horse was still ahead, to be sure, but Peg was gradually gaining on him.

"Please do hurry," Crissy breathed.

It seemed that Peg had been trying to catch up with the bay horse for a long time now, although Crissy knew that it couldn't really have been more than a minute. The bay horse was first now, and Peg was rapidly overtaking the little spotted horse in second place. The rest of the racers were trailing behind, although not by much.

"I should have brought Susan-Cat. Peg just loves to hear her purr when we're going fast," thought Crissy as Peg came up behind Jethro Blade and the bay horse. "Oh!"

Peg skidded on an icy patch, almost lost her balance, caught herself in time, and raced on, but the bay horse and two others were now ahead of her. Crissy could already see her muff gone and herself in disgrace with Aunt Henrietta.

"Peg!" she cried. "Peg! Listen!"

Crissy leaned forward, so Peg would be sure to hear, and purred as loudly as she could. Peg cocked an interested ear and went a little faster.

"All right, Peg," Papa repeated. "Let's pick up our feet this time!"

Peg edged past two of the lead horses, but the bay horse was now almost half a block ahead. Crissy purred louder. Elmo said nothing as Peg drew closer to the bay horse, but his eyes were wide with excitement. Jethro Blade glanced over his shoulder and saw Peg almost breathing down the back of his neck. He stood up in his sleigh and lashed the bay horse with his whip.

"Get going, you!" he yelled angrily.

The bay horse, his eyes rolling in excitement, reared and overturned the sleigh, tipping Jethro Blade neatly into a pile of snow in front of the Mercantile. Peg swept on past and crossed the finish line far ahead of everybody. Crissy sighed and buried her nose in her muff, sniffing its furry softness.

"Whoopee!" yelled Elmo. "We won!"

Crissy brought a red apple out of her muff, climbed out of the sleigh again, and gave it to Peg.

"You're a nice horse!" Crissy told her. "A perfectly lovely horse!"

Peg whinnied, nibbled delicately at the apple, and graciously accepted the wreath of evergreen which the mayor slid around her neck. Crissy began hunting for Aunt Henrietta. Looking rather pink, her aunt was standing on the sidewalk beside Dr. Agnew, who was smiling his rather acid smile and saying something in a low voice.

"Still the perfectly turned out lady, I see," Crissy thought he said.

That was exactly what Aunt Henrietta was, Crissy thought, but for some reason Dr. Agnew didn't seem to like it. Crissy, who was pressed close to Dr. Agnew's back by the pushing crowd, couldn't help hearing his next words.

"Somebody'll muss your hair some day or rumple your dress," he muttered, "and then where'll you be?"

"I—I— Oh, Chauncey!" Aunt Henrietta stammered. "Don't be so— But you always were, never caring about having things nice."

" 'Nice' is fine," said Dr. Agnew, "but not prissy, Henrietta. I do hate—"

"Oh, dear!" thought Crissy. "They're quarreling, and

right in the middle of a crowd on River Street, too. But thank goodness, not very loud."

Mr. Wellfleet began pushing his way through the swarm of people.

"Well, well," he said when he saw Aunt Henrietta. "Where's Crissy? Quite the little schemer, she is. Everybody's talking about—"

"Here I am!" cried Crissy.

She signaled desperately to Mr. Wellfleet behind Aunt Henrietta's back. Anybody, she thought, should know better than to tell Aunt Henrietta about that bet. Crissy shushed him loudly and hoped that he understood. He nodded wisely.

"Only little girl that got to ride in the races," he said hastily. "Quite an honor, especially such a close race. Well, I'll have to be going along. I—"

"Clang! Clang! Clang!" The sound of the firebell rang out over the town. "Clang! Clang! Clang!"

Most of the men who had been racing simply kept on racing, this time toward the firehouse, and the ones who had been watching took off after them on foot. Nearly every able-bodied man in town was a volunteer fireman, and those who weren't always tagged along to see where the fire was and to give free advice about how to fight it. Crissy saw Papa, Elmo, and the sleigh vanishing down the street.

"Oh, dear!" she wailed. "I wanted to go, too!"

"Congratulations on a noble race!" said Dr. Agnew. "It was your encouragement, I'm sure, that made Peg win."

"I purred," said Crissy simply. "Where do you suppose the fire is?"

"Let's go and see," Dr. Agnew suggested. "Cassius has Rex over here somewhere. Will you come, Henrietta?"

Although Dr. Agnew spoke as though he thought she wouldn't, Aunt Henrietta, her cheeks bright crimson, climbed into the doctor's sleigh, which he had had painted red with little gold bells stenciled on for a border. Dr. Agnew took the reins from Cassius.

"You can go on home, Cassius," he said. "Take the rest of the day off."

"Smoke!" cried Crissy in excitement. "Lots of smoke!"

A dark cloud was mushrooming high into the sky. Dr. Agnew took the back street and hurried in the direction of the smoke. He finally leaned out to ask a running boy about the fire.

"It's Wellfleet's Carriage Works," yelled the boy, running even faster. "Everything's burning up!"

All the way downtown, Crissy sat with her mouth open, not able to say a word. She felt exactly the way she had the time Elmo bumped into her and knocked all the breath out of her. Dr. Agnew left the sleigh and Rex up the street from the Works.

"Never know how far a fire will spread," he explained.

Crissy jumped out and ran, with Dr. Agnew and his medicine case one jump behind her, and Aunt Henrietta trailing only a little way behind. Even in the excitement, Crissy had time to be surprised at how fast Aunt Henrietta could run.

Crissy managed to wriggle her way through the crowd and slide down the alley to the back of the plant. Already the smoke was seeping out in dangerous-looking wisps from around the front door, and flames showed at one or two side windows.

"The paint shop," said Crissy. "Oh, dear!"

The volunteer firemen were busy with hose laid from the fire hydrant and extra ones from the river, where the old steam fire engine was pumping water the way it used to before there was any city water in Granite City. Crissy had never seen the old steamer in use before, because nowadays it was brought out only for big fires when there were not enough fire hydrants for all the hose lines that the firemen needed.

"Out of the way, little girl!" said a gruff voice. "Oh, it's you! Here, you can help push!"

It was Old Man Douglas, the blacksmith, pulling a finished carriage out of the paint shop.

"Can't expect those painters to look after their own business," he grumbled. "Even in a fire, they have to depend on the smiths. Here, give it another push. I have to go in and get some more out."

"Papa!" said Crissy breathlessly. "Where's Papa?"

"Getting out the horseless carriages, I guess," Old Man Douglas yelled. "Anyway, he was. There's one sitting over there now."

Sure enough, one shining Wellfleet automobile was safe in the snowy vacant lot next to the Works. It was surrounded by an assortment of road carts, wagons, and half-finished carriages which the workmen, assisted by the firemen and a bedraggled Elmo, were hauling out of the flaming building. The snow around the Works was melting into mud from the heat of the fire and from the many tramping feet as the volunteers, damp and dirty, rushed with their hose from one part of the plant to another. Still the flames and smoke rose higher and higher.

Crissy heard the sound of a motor, and Papa came roaring through the big double doors with another Wellfleet, which sputtered and bucked its way through the snow to join the other machine in the vacant lot.

"Two more!" said Papa breathlessly. "Back in a minute!"

Crissy and Elmo helped push more unfinished surreys and wagons to the vacant lot. Crissy would have liked to go inside to help carry out tools, but the fire chief, Captain Dowling, who was directing the work on that side of the building, refused to let her nearer than twenty feet from the blazing shop.

"Walls might fall in," he said, "or out, which would be worse. Well, bless my soul, what's this coming?"

Grogarty, the painter, assisted by Jed Haley, was carrying Old Man Douglas's anvil and hammer out of the smith shop.

"There!" said Grogarty. "The foundation of the carriage business—to hear you tell it!"

Old Man Douglas looked at the anvil affectionately and then at his enemies from the paint shop.

"There's something to be said for paint, too," he stated grudgingly. "I'm obliged to you."

Papa, looking very red in the face, came out with the third Wellfleet, and everybody lent a hand to push it through the muddy snow to safety.

"One more," said Papa, "and then—"

"No more," said Captain Dowling firmly. "It's no place for anybody in there now." He gave a piercing whistle to call his volunteers to safety. "Everybody out. Can't do anything more."

Crissy was fond of Captain Dowling, who looked just the way she thought a fire chief should look—tall and dignified with a trim gray mustache and blue eyes which could look as cold as ice or could twinkle with warm laughter.

Mr. Wellfleet struggled out of his plant the last of all, carrying the ledgers. He laid them on the back seat of a red farm wagon and covered them carefully with his overcoat. His face looked drawn and tired.

"Some days," he said wearily, "you can't lay up a cent. Some days, in fact—"

The flames seemed to leap even higher, and with a crash the whole side of the building fell in.

"Oh!" Crissy gave a frightened cry and burst into tears. "It'll never be the same, never at all!"

"It'll be better," said Mr. Wellfleet stoutly. "Haley, you spread the word around. All hands here first thing in the morning to clear away the mess and get ready to build again. I guess if we can build carriages we can build a new carriage works, too."

"Yes, sir!" said Jed. "There's nothing like building something to put new vigor into people." He grinned at Crissy. " 'Variety's the very spice of life.' (William Cowper, born 1731, died 1800.) No time for fussing at present, anyway. You've got a bet to collect."

Jed steered her briskly around the outskirts of the crowd in search of Jethro Blade. She caught a glimpse of Dr. Agnew working over one of the firemen who had been overcome by smoke. She was surprised to see Aunt Henrietta, with her best hat over one eye, kneeling beside him handing him things from his medicine bag.

"There he is! Blade!" bellowed Jed. "You may as well take possession of that new automobile right now while it's handy. Just tie a stout rope on the back of your sleigh and tow your machine home."

Jethro began to sputter.

"Lot of nonsense! Probably damaged in the fire and won't run even when spring comes. Just foolishness, that silly bet. Why, nobody—"

Crissy tugged at Jed's sleeve. She had an idea which might work and might also relieve her conscience of having sold an automobile on a bet.

"Mr. Blade," she said, "we were only teasing. You don't have to buy that automobile. On account of one machine burning up, there aren't but three for sale in the whole town, and people will be practically fighting to get them, because nobody knows when there'll be any more." She smiled sweetly upon him. "So just forget all about it."

She and Jed started off through the crowd again.

"Hey!" Jethro Blade bawled after them. "Wait up a minute. I didn't actually say I wouldn't buy one, did I? A scarce article like that might be worth considerable. I won't say for sure I want one, but—"

"Suit yourself," said Crissy. "I guess I'll go and see how many Papa's sold already. I wouldn't be surprised but that they're all gone, anyway."

When they got back to the Wellfleets, Crissy was astonished to find that Papa actually had sold one to an old farmer who had also decided that automobiles were going to be scarce in Granite City. The old man was already towing it off behind his cutter and team. Jethro Blade came bustling up.

"Hey!" he said to Papa. "One of those is mine! And don't go selling it out from under me, either. I bargained for this machine with your daughter here, and I won't be—"

Jed Haley caught Papa's eye and winked, and Papa immediately began acting reluctant.

"Don't know whether I can let you have one or not," he said. "This is the first I heard about any deal for one, but maybe— Crissy, did I actually promise that man out on the Wesley Road, or do you think we could get him to wait a while?"

"I guess we could," said Crissy, who knew perfectly well that the man on the Wesley Road had told Papa that he wouldn't risk his life in a horseless carriage if they were giving them away like soap premiums. "You didn't really promise."

"It's a deal then," said Jethro Blade. "I'll take it with me behind my sleigh so's it won't get away from me, and I'll make out a check for it right now."

Aunt Henrietta came hurrying up to Papa.

"Could I go home now?" she asked. "People will be coming, and nothing ready."

Crissy had forgotten all about the New Year's calls and the collations all over town. She looked reluctantly back at the smoking ruins, but she went obediently along to help Aunt Henrietta.

"I'll be home later," said Papa.

It was very much later when he came, so late that almost all the New Year's callers had gone home after dining lavishly on Aunt Henrietta's bountiful food. Papa was accompanied by Dr. Agnew, Mr. Wellfleet, and Jed Haley, all looking very wet, dirty and cold. They came in by the back door and sat wearily around the kitchen table.

"Hot coffee, please, Hen," said Papa, "and anything else you've got. We're hungrier than a pack of wolves."

For a few minutes, Aunt Henrietta and Crissy flew back and forth from dining room to kitchen, seeing off the last guests and feeding the hungry men at the same time. Then Aunt Henrietta locked the front door, put on her apron, and began fixing ham and eggs.

"Nothing delicate," she decided, "not after all you've been through."

She didn't even bat an eye when Jed Haley lit up his cigar after his third cup of coffee. Jed's hat, for a wonder, was carefully placed under his chair instead of on his head.

" 'Blessed hour of our dinners!' " he said. "(Owen Meredith, born 1831, died 1891.)"

"I hear you're an expert on literature," said Aunt Henrietta amiably. "You must come and speak to the Ladies' Shakespeare Club some day."

Jed looked alarmed.

"I couldn't do that, ma'am," he said, "but maybe I could do something better for you some time. If you ever need to raise a little money for something, get in touch with me. I might have an idea."

"I'll do that." Aunt Henrietta poured everybody another cup of coffee and looked at the mountain of dirty dishes in the kitchen sink. "You men go ahead and finish. Clarissa Jane, get the dishpan."

In the end, Dr. Agnew rolled up his sleeves and washed the dishes, Papa and Jed Haley dried, and Crissy and Aunt Henrietta put away. Mr. Wellfleet, profuse in his thanks for the food, went home to draw up a plan for the new carriage works.

"By the way, Crissy," said Papa. "I sold the other machine, too. One of our carriage dealers from Hilltown came over for the race and ordered it for a customer of his."

"Three in one day!" cried Crissy. "That's wonderful!"

" 'Tisn't bad," Papa agreed. "And I'm proud of the way

you sold that one to Jethro Blade. That was real think-ing, figuring out what he'd do under the circumstances."

"Don't speak of it." Crissy glanced anxiously over her shoulder to make sure that Aunt Henrietta couldn't hear. "You know as well as I do that selling automobiles isn't ladylike." She grinned at Papa. "Martha May would never dream of doing such a thing."

7

HIGH WATER

"Looks like rain." Elmo gazed intently at the sky. "Well, are you coming, or aren't you?"

He strode off on towering four-foot stilts, and Crissy followed awkwardly on her new three-foot ones. Elmo claimed that stilts were fun, but Crissy, now that she had some, wasn't quite so sure. It was true that she felt delightfully tall, but she also felt uncomfortably wobbly.

"Just like springtime," said Elmo. "Snow all gone,

weather warm, even if it isn't quite April yet. Guess I'll have to get out my bag of marbles and practice up some."

"It's too muddy." Crissy was puffing along behind him, trying hard to keep up. "Everything's soaking wet on account of the snow melting."

"It'll dry off." Nothing was bothering Elmo very much this morning. "I'll practice on the parlor rug, anyway. Hey, let's cut across Garretts' back yard. It's shorter."

Crissy didn't know shorter to where, since they weren't going anywhere in particular, but she followed obediently. She never would have learned how to walk on stilts, even as badly as she did, if Elmo hadn't taught her. She stalked jauntily along the Garretts' driveway, which was paved with cinders and rather bumpy underfoot, and then started to follow Elmo kitty-corners across to the alley.

"Hey, look!" yelled Elmo. "I can run!"

He capered across the yard with long steps like a giant in a hurry.

"Well, I can't!" cried Crissy. "Elmo! Wait!"

Her stilts seemed heavier than ever—so heavy, in fact, that she could hardly lift them. She and Elmo had both forgotten that the Garretts' yard was lower than most people's and that all the melting snow had left the ground unusually soggy. Elmo had moved so fast that he had skipped safely across, but when Crissy tried to pull one stilt out of the ground, it stuck fast and even sank in deeper. It leaned farther and farther away from her until she let go of it entirely and clung for a terrifying moment to the other stilt like a monkey on a stick. Then she and the remaining stilt fell flat in the mud of the Garretts' back yard. Elmo descended from his stilts and ran back to Crissy.

"Girls!" he snorted. "Always falling on their faces!"

Crissy sat up and mopped mud out of her eyes.

"Who wanted to cut across here?" she sputtered. "We were doing just fine before that. We— Oh, dear, here comes Mrs. Garrett!"

Mrs. Garrett and Martha May were both standing on the back porch, making clucking noises of disapproval. Crissy got up and mopped herself with Elmo's bandanna.

"I'm sorry if I made a dent in your yard," she told Mrs. Garrett. "I—I didn't know it was so soft."

Mrs. Garrett looked at the holes which the stilts had made, and Crissy hurriedly scooped up some mud to repair the damage.

"I'd ask you in for some cookies if you weren't so dirty," said Martha May smugly.

"Thank you just the same," said Crissy. "Give Elmo some, why don't you? He's quite clean."

"No, I'm not." Elmo skidded as though by accident and put out his hands to catch himself as he fell. "I'm just as

Santa Clara County Free Library
San Jose, Calif.

dirty as she is." He looked at Crissy and began to grin. "Almost, I mean. Nobody could be—"

Crissy gave him a look, carried her stilts to the driveway, climbed up on them, and started for home.

"So glad to have seen you," she told Mrs. Garrett and Martha May.

She guessed that would show them that she could be a perfect lady even when covered with mud. At the thought of how funny she must look, Crissy couldn't help grinning to herself, in spite of knowing that there would be nothing to grin about when Aunt Henrietta saw her. Elmo came striding up beside her.

"Come on to my house," he said. "Mama'll help clean you up."

Crissy followed him gratefully. In spite of all his fussing about girls, Elmo always stuck by her in time of trouble. She took off her shoes on the Hawkins' back porch and padded into the kitchen in her stocking feet. Mrs. Hawkins took one look at her and burst into laughter.

"You look like those men in blackface at the minstrel show," she declared. "Come over here close to the hot water, and we'll start scrubbing. Elmo, you clean her shoes —and your own, too, while you're about it. Here, have some gingerbread if you think you can get it into your mouth without any mud."

Crissy stood obediently while Mrs. Hawkins dipped hot

water out of the reservoir on the stove and began scrubbing Crissy's hands and face.

"Hang your sweater on this chair beside the stove," Mrs. Hawkins advised. "Most of that mud will brush off when it's good and dry. Goodness, couldn't you have picked any other place but Mrs. Garrett's yard?"

"I guess not," said Crissy. "Martha May was home, too, looking extra clean."

"Naturally," said Mrs. Hawkins. "Oh, dear, the baby's waking up."

"I'll go get her," Crissy offered.

As she lifted the baby out of her crib and carried her out to the kitchen, Crissy wished that all grownups were like Mrs. Hawkins, not bothered by mud-covered children or anything else. Crissy looked apologetically at the smears on the kitchen floor.

"Give me a rag and I'll mop it up," she said.

"Do that, and I'll give the baby her bottle." Mrs. Hawkins settled herself comfortably in the low rocker beside the window. "How's the automobile business these days?"

"Well, Papa has some prospects," Crissy told her, "but he's been busy helping build the new carriage works. Anyway, people don't want automobiles until the roads dry out."

The new plant was really lovely, Crissy thought, although maybe not so interesting as the old one, which had been just messy enough so that Crissy always expected something surprising to turn up under a pile of scraps that had been lying in a corner for years. Now there were no unswept corners, because the men were all so proud of the new building they had built with their own hands that they kept it swept to what Crissy considered unnecessary neatness. A few of the men had even taken to wearing neckties to work, but Jed Haley reported that most of the force thought this was carrying things a little too far.

The new building was brick, with light streaming in from windows on all four sides. All the way across the front, Mr. Wellfleet had built a huge show window, which contained one Wellfleet automobile and one of his fanciest carriages, the latter drawn by a life-sized model of a dappled gray horse which he had had made to order in Chicago. The horse was mounted on a little platform with roller skate wheels underneath so it could be easily moved.

The men made a lot of fun of the model, but they acted rather proud of it, all the same, and Jed Haley produced all sorts of quotations from the poets in honor of that noble beast, the horse.

"Too bad the poets never said anything about automobiles," Crissy complained one day.

Jed thought a minute.

"It's too soon," he said, "but some of the things they did say would fit pretty well." He grinned widely at Crissy.

"For instance, 'Take heed, for heaven's sake, take heed,' by you-know-who, would apply very nicely."

While Elmo went out to attend to the new batch of rabbits he had bought, Crissy settled herself closer to Mrs. Hawkins' stove and told her all about how the men had built the new plant, with everybody turning to and working like mad.

"Even the smiths and the painters didn't fight much," said Crissy, "though they did argue some about how the fire started. Old Man Douglas said everybody knows that paint cans are always setting things on fire, and Grogarty said that those sparks from the smiths' fires blow all over, and Old Man Douglas said that Jed Haley's cigar was enough to burn the whole place down, even though he hadn't been in the paint shop since the day before."

"Are they making everything again?" Mrs. Hawkins asked.

"More carriages than anything else," Crissy said, "because Mr. Wellfleet says it's mainly a carriage works, not an automobile factory, but he has three or four automobiles ready, so Papa'll have something to sell when he can get at it."

"He'll do fine," said Mrs. Hawkins. "We'd buy one ourselves if we could afford it."

Walking home in dry clothes, Crissy felt better about everything after her visit with Mrs. Hawkins. Still, she did wish that Papa could sell some cars. Time was getting short before the Jubilee—only a trifle over three months—and Crissy couldn't imagine how Papa could sell sixteen more automobiles in that time.

Crissy just made it to the front door before another rain storm came up. Rain dashed against the window panes and ran down the street in big streams, but by the time Crissy had rebraided her hair and changed into a fresh dress the rain had stopped and the sun was out again.

"Such odd weather for the time of year," said Aunt Henrietta, who was hemming a dish towel beside the kitchen window. "I'll have to start spring house cleaning if this keeps up."

Crissy sighed. Spring house cleaning was dreadful, she thought, because of Aunt Henrietta's being so very thorough. She went over each room methodically, moving all the furniture out, cleaning the wallpaper, washing every inch of the woodwork and floor, and taking up the carpets and putting them over the line for Papa to beat. Everything smelled wonderful—like fresh air and laundry soap—when she got through, but while she was doing it there was no peace for anybody.

Papa stuck his head inside and yelled for Crissy.

"Want to go selling automobiles with me?"

"In this weather?" Aunt Henrietta protested.

"If I can pull it off in this weather, it'll be all the better.

Proves that the Wellfleet doesn't stop for anything—or not much."

Crissy was surprised to see that Papa had left Peg in the barn and was driving one of the new Wellfleets.

"It's muddy," Papa warned as she climbed in, "so don't brush against the wheel." He gave the crank two or three violent turns, and the motor started obediently. "She's all tuned up, ready for anything. We're going out in the country, out to the Rivals'."

The Rivals were two men who had built huge houses directly opposite each other in one of the best farming areas around Granite City. Nobody knew what had started them off at trying to outdo each other, but they had been at it for years, Papa said. Their names were Mr. Dean and Mr. Davis, but nearly everybody had forgotten that and just called them the Rivals.

Mr. Dean, Papa recalled, had inherited some money and had immediately spent it on an elaborate three-story house with all the porches and stained glass windows and curlicues that the architect could think of. Mr. Davis immediately sold off his wood lot and used that money for a house that was just as big as Mr. Dean's and had a tower room besides and his initials done in stained glass on the front door. Luckily, the Rivals had good crops for several years, because after the houses were done they built barns, and after that they grew hedges trimmed in fantastic shapes like swans and ships and sphinxes, and after that one of them bought a pedigreed horse, so that the other one had to have one too.

"And then it was fancy carriages," said Papa, "which was where I came in. Neither one of them will buy anything but the best, for fear the other one will get ahead of him.

One of them—I forget which now—ordered a carriage once
with Oriental carpet on the floor, which is about as silly
as you can get. And so I have a feeling that with the right
conversation we might be able to sell an automobile or
two."

"My goodness, that creek's high!"

Crissy looked at the muddy water swirling just under
the floor of a little bridge as the Wellfleet clattered across.

"Spring freshets," said Papa absently. "Let's see, maybe

I better try Dean first. Hold on to your hat. I want to arrive with a flourish."

Papa speeded up the Wellfleet, squeezed the big rubber
bulb which made the new horn bleat like a startled sheep,
and rounded the driveway into Deans' with a fine spatter
of gravel.

"You wait here until I persuade Mr. Dean to go for a
ride with me. Then I want you to wander over to the
Davises' and tell them that Mr. Dean is thinking about
buying an automobile, which he will be by that time.
Then just wait for me there. As I remember, Mrs. Davis
makes pretty good cookies and likes children, besides."

Crissy nodded. It was fun to help Papa sell automobiles
and especially exciting when he had his mind made up to
sell two at once. Through the hedge, she could hear Mr.
Dean saying, "Automobiles! Just rich men's playthings!"

"Well?" said Papa in a flattering tone. " 'Tisn't a poor
man that has a place like this one of yours."

"Next thing you'll be trying to sell me a yacht or a string
of pearls." Mr. Dean's voice stopped for a minute and then
went on. "Well, it is a nice house, if I do say so."

"Come and take a ride with me, why don't you?" Papa
urged. "I want you to see how this machine goes, even if
you're not of a mind to buy one."

Crissy slid hastily out of the seat and strolled over to the
Davises'. Sure enough, Mrs. Davis was just taking a pan

of cookies out of the oven, and she established Crissy at the kitchen table with a stack of cookies and a glass of cold milk. Mr. Davis came in shortly, and Crissy got a chance to tell him about Papa taking Mr. Dean out for an automobile ride.

"He'd likely be idiot enough to buy one, just for the show," Mr. Davis snorted. "I never did see such a man to want to outdo a person." He thoughtfully munched on a cookie. "Tell your father to be sure to see me before he goes home, will you?"

"Yes, sir," said Crissy politely. "I'll tell him."

She could hardly conceal her excitement when Papa appeared from the direction of the Deans', gave her a triumphant wink, and went out to the barn to talk to Mr. Davis. At last, Crissy rode out with Papa between the fancy stone gateposts.

"Success!" Papa announced. "I sold an automobile to Dean and an automobile and a motor wagon to Davis to haul his corn to town with. Just a minute, now, while I break the news to Dean about the motor wagon."

By the time they were finally ready to go home, Mr. Dean also had ordered a motor wagon slightly larger than Mr. Davis's, and Papa was pretending to have tonsillitis from talking so much.

"Four!" Crissy exclaimed. "Just like that! Let's see, it's

eight altogether, and twelve more to go! Oh, Papa, do you think—"

"Never doubt that success is just around the corner," said Papa jubilantly, "although I must admit I don't know any more people like the Rivals that I can work on. Maybe you can think of some while I see a few out-of-town prospects next week."

"If I get a good prospect, will you let me ride in the Diamond Jubilee parade with you?" Crissy asked. "In a Wellfleet, I mean?"

"I surely will," Papa promised. "I was planning on leaving Peg for Hen, anyway, unless we can get Hen to ride with us by that time."

Crissy was doubtful about anything like that ever happening, and, anyway, Peg would certainly have her feelings hurt if she was not allowed to draw a decorated carriage in the parade.

"Well!" said Papa. "Take a look at that, will you?"

They had come again to the little stream which had been lapping at the bottom of the bridge when they had crossed on their way to the Rivals'. Now a stream of water was pouring over the floor of the bridge.

"Who'd have thought it?" Papa exclaimed. "Well, it's not very deep yet, and I certainly intend to sleep at home tonight, so here we go!"

The Wellfleet made it across all right, although Crissy

had an uneasy moment when the bridge swayed under their wheels and the boggy road on the other side seemed to be snatching at the Wellfleet to keep it from going ahead. As they drove through town, it began to rain again, and Crissy saw that the Granite River was crawling closer to the red paint mark which showed the highest point the water had ever come up on the big iron bridge.

"I shan't be surprised if I have to swim to the Works one of these mornings," said Papa. "These streams are rising fast."

Crissy said nothing, because she was trying to think of people who might need automobiles—or anyway want them even if they didn't need them. The Hawkins wanted one, only they didn't have the money. Mrs. Garrett would probably want one if she thought everybody else had one, which of course was far from the case. Mr. Cassoway, the banker, ought to want one, just because he was the second richest man in town, but since he never went anywhere except to the bank even with his horse and carriage, she supposed he wasn't such a likely prospect, either. Of course, his wife belonged to all the clubs in town, so maybe she and Mrs. Garrett could both be persuaded by the same argument about fashion. Aunt Henrietta could be such a help, if only she liked automobiles, but so far she didn't seem the least bit interested.

Aunt Henrietta was waiting for them at the front door.

"Where in the world have you been?" she demanded. "The Diamond Jubilee committee has to raise some more money for the decorations, and I wanted you to take me up to talk to Mr. Haley about those marionettes of his, seeing he was nice enough to offer. I was supposed to go today and report back tomorrow, and now it's too late."

"Peg couldn't make it before supper because it's uphill all the way and muddy besides," Papa agreed. "Guess you'll have to go tomorrow." He looked quizzically at his sister. "It wouldn't be too late if we went in the machine. We could be up there and back before dark as easy as not."

"All right, I'll do it." Aunt Henrietta put on her hat with the air of a woman about to have a tooth pulled. "If I must, I must. It's really quite important."

Papa winked at Crissy.

"Let's go, then. Crissy, you better stay home and watch the supper. We'll need nourishment after such a danger-ous expedition."

Crissy wanted to go, too, but it would have been crowded and she agreed with Papa that Aunt Henrietta should be introduced to automobiling in as much comfort as possible.

"The fried potatoes are sitting on the back of the stove," Aunt Henrietta called. "Stir them around once in a while, will you?"

It didn't seem very long before Papa was back, but Aunt Henrietta was not with him.

"Dish up the supper," said Papa. "Hen went off with Dr. Agnew in his Wellfleet to eat at the hotel."

"She did?" said Crissy in astonishment.

"Yep, she did," said Papa. "We got up to Jed's all right and she arranged for him to give his puppet show for the Jubilee committee—very cultural, she said—and then when we were almost home Chauncey drove up beside us and got to talking, and the first thing I knew Hen was riding off with him."

"How did she like the automobile?

"Never batted an eye, even when we almost got stuck down in the Flats. The creek down there is rising, too, so it's muddy and in some places just plain wet. All she said when we got on the other side was 'She made it all right, didn't she?' So I think we have a convert."

Crissy was sure of it when Aunt Henrietta, looking pink and excited, came home at the unholy hour of nine o'clock and brought Dr. Agnew in for a piece of chocolate cake.

"I shall certainly tell Mrs. Garrett about automobiling," she announced. "So much time saved, and they're all the fashion in New York, Chauncey says."

"So have I been saying for a couple of years or so," said Papa plaintively, "but nobody would ever listen."

Aunt Henrietta flushed even pinker and brought everybody another piece of cake.

"Clarissa Jane!" she said suddenly. "You go on to bed! You know you're not allowed to stay up past eight-thirty."

"Yes, ma'am," said Crissy meekly.

She stole a look under her eyelashes at Papa, who gave her his blankest expression, but she did catch what was unmistakably a wink from Dr. Agnew. She awoke once in the night to hear rain pounding on the roof. In the morning it was still drizzling, and water was standing in a big pool in front of the house.

"Your father says you may come downtown to see the flood," said Aunt Henrietta at breakfast. "River Street's about under, with all this rain and the ice melting in the river besides, so he went down early to see what he could do to help out. You're to take Elmo with you and go straight to the Works so he can keep an eye on you, because it's dangerous some places."

As Crissy whooped out of the house and over to Elmo's, she thought how fortunate it was that the flood had arrived in the middle of spring vacation so nobody would have to miss the excitement because of arithmetic and spelling.

Elmo and Crissy, wearing the rubber boots which Papa had left for them, went down to the Branch first and saw that it had entirely overflowed its banks and had spread all over the little ravine which was also the town park. The iron deer which usually stood so majestically on a little slope looked as though he were swimming through the muddy water, with only his head and antlers out, and the park benches had disappeared entirely.

"Won't float," said Elmo, "on account of being iron. So I guess they're under all that mud and water."

The closer they came to River Street the worse things looked. Crissy and Elmo had to go several blocks out of the way to get to the Works at all. Huge blocks of ice were piled up back of the railroad bridge, and water poured around this ice jam over the top of the bridge and into River Street. At the Works everybody was scurrying around trying to put things safely away.

"First fire and then water," Mr. Wellfleet sputtered as he waded angrily through several inches of muddy water in the main office. "Don't know which is worse, but it certainly has our schedules all messed up. We'll never get our orders filled if this keeps up. Here, Crissy, put the wastebaskets on top of my desk."

Elmo and Crissy left Mr. Wellfleet saving his ledgers again and went out into the shop to see what they could do there. The fires in the blacksmith shop had already been drowned out, water was lapping around the paint cans in the paint shop, and scraps of wood were floating like little boats around the wood shop. Several men were hoisting carriages and road carts up on platforms made out of saw horses and pieces of timber.

"Not that it'll do any good," said Mr. Wellfleet gloomily. "Probably the whole place will fall to pieces and float down the river."

"Not brick, will it?" Crissy whispered fearfully to Papa.

"It might possibly fall apart," said Papa, "but it will never in this world float."

Outside, Crissy heard a "boom" as the fire department dynamited the ice behind the bridge. Water rushed through the gap and spread farther up River Street, and more ice swept down from farther upstream and jammed up behind the bridge again. Crissy and Elmo opened a window and leaned out to look. As usual, Dr. Agnew was in the thick of things, carrying his little black bag.

"For wet feet and such," he told Crissy. "A very damp climate here today."

Captain Dowling was busy, too, and the police chief, Clem Hanson, in his blue uniform with the gold buttons. Suddenly Crissy had a wonderful idea.

"Captain Dowling," she said, "why don't you buy an automobile for the fire department? Or a motor wagon? You could get to fires a lot quicker."

"If you got there at all," said Clem Hanson, who, Crissy remembered, did not like automobiles nor the people who drove them.

"Policemen use them in New York," Crissy argued.

"Policemen don't use them here," said Clem sharply, "nor aren't going to."

"Never?" asked Crissy dolefully.

"Not while I've got my strength. Supposing the thing broke down?"

"Supposing a wheel came off the patrol wagon, too?" said Crissy. "Or suppose—"

"Well, I've got no time to be arguing with children," Clem Hanson said sourly to Captain Dowling, "even if you have. We're here to clear that ice jam."

He splashed off after more dynamite.

"No sale," said Dr. Agnew, "though I must say you tried."

Captain Dowling leaned toward Crissy.

"I'd just as lief have one for the fire department," he said. "Might have saved a house the other day if we could have made it there a little sooner. Won't hurt for me to ask the aldermen at the next meeting."

"Oh, will you?" Crissy cried in delight. "You really will? Oh, thank you!"

She rushed off in wild excitement to find Papa.

"Boom!" went another charge of dynamite, and ice from behind the bridge flew in all directions. "Boom! Boom! Boom!"

"Papa!" Crissy yelled above the sound of the explosions. "Papa! I sold another machine, maybe."

"To Captain Dowling, for the fire department," Elmo put in.

"Well, but—" Papa began.

"If the aldermen say so," said Crissy.

"Oh," said Papa.

"You think they will, don't you?" cried Crissy in alarm.

"Hard to tell with aldermen," said Papa.

"Who is one?" asked Crissy.

"Chauncey is," said Papa, "and some others that I don't know very well. Guess I'd better do some talking beforehand, and go to the meeting besides." He patted Crissy's shoulder. "You did fine, youngster. It's just that you can't ever tell how voting will turn out, especially if what you want is going to cost some money."

"I guess not." Crissy sighed. "Well, it was a good idea while it lasted, anyway."

" 'So vanishes the glory of the world,' " said Jed Haley. "(Translated from the Latin by one Jed Haley.)"

Crissy was just hoping that Jed was not going to expect her to remember quotations from Latin as well as English when an extra loud "Boom!" came from outside. With a great swoosh, the last of the ice rushed from behind the bridge, followed by a wall of dammed-up water that swept down the river channel, over the floor boards of the bridge, and down River Street in a rushing stream.

"Just the way Papa said it did before," Crissy cried. "Oh, my, isn't it exciting?"

"Flood's over," said Captain Dowling cheerfully,

"though I must admit it doesn't look like it at the moment. Aside from mud, though, things'll look just about the same as usual tomorrow."

"Bother!" said Elmo. "I did hope the school might get washed away!"

8

THE BIRTHDAY SURPRISE

"Easy, there!" said Jed Haley. "Never run into a cow unless you're driving something bigger than the cow—which you aren't."

Crissy steered the Wellfleet nervously around a black-and-white cow and wondered whether learning to drive an automobile was such a good idea after all. She had planned it for Papa's birthday surprise, but the only person who had been surprised so far was Crissy, who had thought that driving was easy when it wasn't at all. Still, Papa's birthday wasn't until June fifteenth, which left a little over two weeks in which to subdue the Wellfleet.

" 'Order,' " said Jed, " 'is heaven's first law.' (Alexander Pope, born 1688, died 1744.) Especially when you're driving an automobile. So we'll just stop right here and go over everything again."

Crissy thought that it was easy enough to recite what she was supposed to do, but much harder to do it, especially when she kept thinking of what would happen if she made even one small mistake. Some of the things already had happened and some, luckily, had not.

"First," said Crissy glibly, "get ready to begin. Be sure the brake is on, be sure the clutch handle is back, be sure the switch is turned on."

This was easy to remember, because once the clutch handle had not been back and the brake had not been on, and the Wellfleet had started off down the road at the first turn of the crank. If Jed had not been able to leap aboard and yank back on the clutch and brake handles, Crissy supposed that she and the Wellfleet would be going yet.

"Two, open the throttle a little, and crank it up."

"Two, open the throttle a little, and get a good strong man to crank it," Jed corrected. "That's the catch with ladies driving. None of them are strong enough to crank the thing up."

Papa said that sometime somebody would invent a way for machines to start without all that trouble, but sometime, Crissy thought, was no help right now.

"Three, take off the brake and speed up the throttle."

The throttle was a little handle beside the seat that fed the motor more gasoline. Mostly Crissy speeded it up so little that the motor died and Jed had to crank it again, or else so much that the machine seemed about to shake itself to pieces.

"Oh, dear, what next?"

Crissy was glad that Jed was a patient man. Crissy actually was not entitled to driving lessons at all, because she did not own a Wellfleet, but Jed was teaching her at the same time that he tested automobiles.

"You're too young, really," Jed had objected when Crissy first proposed the project, "but there's no law against it that I know of. And I'd be with you every second." He had thought the matter over in silence for a minute. "All right, I'll do it when I'm testing after school or on Saturdays—and out in the country. Don't want any iron fences knocked down here in town."

Jed was always complaining about having three jobs to do at the Works instead of only one, but Crissy was pretty sure that he enjoyed testing the machines almost as much as he did painting stripes on the carriages, and she knew that he liked giving lessons to the new buyers, even though there still weren't very many of them. She was pleased that she had been the one to suggest that everybody who bought a Wellfleet should have free driving lessons as an added inducement to sell more machines. So far it hadn't sold any more, but Mr. Wellfleet did pay Jed extra to give the lessons, so Crissy's idea had done a little good.

"Four," she remembered triumphantly, "press down with your left foot on the left-hand floor pedal, and don't forget to start steering."

At this point things grew complicated, because steering was hard enough without having to keep track of your feet besides. Jed said it was a good deal like steering a bicycle, except that you had either a tiller or a wheel instead of handlebars, but Crissy had never been able to steer bicycles very well, either, usually landing in the Hawkins' raspberry bushes or anywhere else except where she was going. However, with Jed beside her, she had managed so far not to run into anything worse than a small mud puddle.

"And almost a cow," she added conscientiously. "Five, pick your foot up off the left-hand pedal and push forward on the clutch handle."

This made the automobile go even faster, which was pleasant but also made the steering harder. And that was all until it was time to stop, and then—

"Pull the clutch handle back and put your right foot on the brake pedal," Crissy concluded breathlessly.

"All right," said Jed, "let's see you do it. One of these days you'll be so good that I can sit with my feet up and my hat on the back of my head and pretend I have a chauffeur."

"Your *new* hat on the back of your head and an extra fat cigar in your mouth," Crissy reminded him.

That was what Jed said he was going to buy with the extra money from the driving lessons—a new derby and some fatter cigars—but so far he hadn't done it.

"You're so famous now," said Crissy, "that you really need to dress up a little more."

" 'None but himself could be his equal,' " Jed told Crissy smugly. "To tell you the truth, I'm tired of being admired. It was the mistake of my life to give that entertainment for the Jubilee Committee."

An Evening with Shakespeare had been the title of the program which Jed and his marionettes had given at the Globe in the Pinery. Practically all the literary people in town had been there, partly out of curiosity and partly because Aunt Henrietta and her committee had buttonholed everybody who might have fifty cents to spend on culture. Aunt Henrietta had sold so many tickets that she had had to borrow stacks of folding chairs from the undertaker for the occasion. The ladies had taken in more than enough money for their Jubilee decorations and Jed, much to his disgust, had become "a character," with people always waiting around to hear him fit one of his quotations to anything that might be happening.

"That tree won't move," said Jed, "so maybe you'd better."

Crissy jerked the Wellfleet back toward the center of the road. Thinking about Jed's program was hardly necessary, now that it was all over, but she did need to think about Papa's automobiles. With not quite six weeks left before the Jubilee, Crissy was growing more and more alarmed about whether Papa would be able to sell his twenty machines.

"Eight from twenty leaves twelve," Crissy figured for at least the fortieth time, "less one for Mrs. Garrett and one for the mayor and one for the fire department and one for the chief of police makes eight to go. And that's quite a lot."

"It seems to be in Granite City," said Jed. "Let me drive now, if you please. We have some hill climbing to do."

Crissy moved obediently over in the seat. She was glad not to drive for a while, because she needed to think about some more prospects for Papa.

"As though I could think of any he can't," Crissy told herself, "but still I did think of Captain Dowling, even if Papa did most of the talking to the aldermen."

Crissy felt like laughing right out loud whenever she thought of the meeting at which the aldermen had bought not only the motor wagon which Captain Dowling wanted for the fire department but also an automobile for Clem Hanson, the horrified chief of police, who had sat in the meeting and mumbled and objected and fussed, all in vain. The aldermen had gone right ahead and bought him a Wellfleet anyway and told him to learn to drive it.

"Support home industry is my motto," the mayor had declared in a flowery speech which had contained several of Papa's best arguments about the advantages of the automobile. "We want Granite City to be up to the minute in every way, and this is our chance to make a huge stride forward."

"Two strides," Crissy had whispered to Papa, "one for each automobile."

"Up to the minute and into the insane asylum," muttered Clem Hanson, but nobody had paid any attention to him except one alderman, who said "no" in a loud, clear voice when they called for a vote. Some people said afterward that they had heard two "noes" but Crissy knew that one "no" belonged to Clem Hanson, who was struggling to the bitter end, even though he had no right to vote at all.

Papa decided later that Clem was probably right in not wanting an automobile, because no matter how many times

Jed repeated the driving instructions his pupil insisted on pulling back on the tiller and yelling "Whoa" whenever he wanted the Wellfleet to stop.

" 'How use doth breed habit in a man!' " Jed had remarked. "(William Shakespeare, no doubt called Willy by his friends.)"

Jed, having climbed the hill successfully, let Crissy drive some more, insisting that she start and stop in the middle of the road a few more times just for practice.

"And don't forget to blow your horn now and then," said Jed. "It not only shoos people out of the way but advertises the horseless carriage at the same time."

Crissy obediently blew her horn at a dog, who stood defiantly in the middle of the road and barked at her, so that she had to turn out anyway.

"It's a changing world, as your papa so often says," Jed continued. "We used to be a nation of whip-crackers, and now we're turning into horn-blowers instead."

"So many things happen that you don't expect," Crissy complained. "Dogs and trees and cows and ditches and—"

"Be thankful you don't live in Egypt, where they have camels to dodge, too. Anyway, next time will come easier," said Jed reassuringly as he let Crissy off around the corner from home so that Aunt Henrietta wouldn't see her.

Crissy hoped that Jed was right, because up to now she hadn't enjoyed driving a bit except for the queer magic feeling it gave her to be moving down the road as though pushed by an invisible hand.

"Flying would be even more fun," she told Jed.

"Well, you're not a bird yet, so don't be trying that."

Jed tipped his derby and started noisily down the street. Crissy stood still for a minute looking at all the houses around to make sure there were no possible automobile buyers in any of them. Selling things wasn't just luck, she thought soberly. It hadn't been mere happenstance that the mayor had bought himself a Wellfleet and egged the aldermen on to buy two for the city, any more than it had been just happenstance that the Garretts were buying one, too.

The mayor probably never would have thought of it if Papa hadn't sent him a newspaper clipping about a mayor in New York state who drove an automobile on all his city business.

"Which ought to give our own mayor a few ideas," Papa told Crissy.

Papa had also remembered to tell Mrs. Garrett about a distant cousin of hers in Detroit who was driving a new electric automobile.

"Reggie is?" Mrs. Garrett had exclaimed. "Why, I can't imagine it. They never had a nickel when I knew them. Just nobodies. Dear me, I do think—"

"I agree that he's making a mistake to buy an electric,"

Papa said smoothly. "They have their failings—trouble keeping the batteries charged and not much power on muddy roads. A gasoline motor, though—"

"Hmmm," Mrs. Garrett remarked. "Reggie never did have much sense about things like that."

The next day Mr. Garrett had come to Papa and ordered a Wellfleet, not as though he wanted one but as though his wife was trying to get ahead of Cousin Reggie.

"Which of course she is," Aunt Henrietta had reported. "Besides, she decided she'd better hurry because I told her everybody was going to have one before the year was out."

Crissy had looked wonderingly at Papa. None of this sounded the least bit like Aunt Henrietta, who had been acting as gay as the flowers in spring lately. She had even bought herself a big white leghorn hat wreathed with roses and wrapped around with pale blue veiling, a very un-auntish hat indeed.

"My dress!"

Crissy gave up daydreaming on the corner and rushed into the house to start ironing her good white dress, which always took forever because it had rows and rows of lace insertion which Aunt Henrietta had crocheted. It absolutely had to be ready for tomorrow, which was Decoration Day.

"Memorial Day," Crissy corrected herself dutifully, knowing that she would probably keep right on calling it Decoration Day the way she always had.

Crissy liked Decoration Day, even though it was supposed to be sad. She liked to march beside the other school girls, all wearing their white dresses and carrying their little flags to decorate the graves of the Granite City soldiers who had died in the Civil War. It made her feel as though she was part of something big and important when she thought that little girls in the South as well as here in the North were doing the very same things on the very same day.

"Where have you been?" Aunt Henrietta asked. "We have to get those flowers picked ready to take to the cemetery first thing tomorrow morning."

Aunt Henrietta had cut some of the peonies already and set them in buckets of water down cellar where they would keep fresh. Crissy smiled at their pink puffy blossoms, which always reminded her of chubby Grandma Elder out at the farm.

"Better pick some of the red peonies, too, and a big bunch of tulips—the pink ones. And we'll need lilacs, besides, but we'd better wait until morning for them."

Crissy brought in the peonies and tulips and then went back out to pick her own private bouquet which she always took to the cemetery for Mama. Even though Crissy couldn't remember her very well, she was sure that Mama would have liked the little round bouquet which Crissy made each year of dark purple violets edged all around with lilies of the valley and the heart-shaped violet leaves.

In the morning the sun was shining, and Crissy could smell freshly cut grass where Papa had mowed the lawn before breakfast. The big flag was billowing out from the front porch, Peg was tied to the hitching post, and the pails of flowers were sitting on the floor of the surrey. Crissy dived into the white dress, which was so stiffly starched that it could almost stand alone, gave Susan-Cat a farewell pat, and fitted herself into the front seat between Papa and Aunt Henrietta.

The cemetery looked beautiful, too, with everything green and peaceful. Aunt Henrietta hurried around filling the vases on the Bingham lot with water from the old pump, which always hated to give up any water even though Crissy pumped until her arms ached. Crissy arranged her bouquet in the little green vase which she had brought especially for it and sniffed deeply of its fragrance. She slipped her hand comfortingly into Papa's as he stood looking at Mama's flowers. Papa shook his head as though he were bringing himself back from a long way away.

"Well, Hen, time to be going, I guess," he said soberly.

Crissy climbed out of the surrey at the corner downtown to join some girls from her room. She glimpsed the old soldiers of the G.A.R.—"Grand Army of the Republic," she explained to one very small girl who didn't know about the Civil War veterans—in their blue uniforms and their broad-brimmed slouch hats. They always marched at the head of the procession right behind the flag, and those who were lame or too old to walk rode in carriages furnished by the Wellfleet Carriage Works.

"Senator missed the train from the Junction," somebody called across the street, "and there isn't another until afternoon."

The senator, who was the speaker of the day, was coming home from Washington especially to give the Decoration Day oration.

"Papa—" Crissy began, but Papa had already stepped up and offered to go after the senator in one of the Wellfleets.

"Back in about an hour," he promised as he headed for the Works to get out one of the machines. "Better march out to the cemetery without him and plan to have his speech the last thing. Hen, you'll have to drive Peg to the speaking yourself."

When Papa came back with the senator, Crissy, standing in the crowd, was not much surprised to see the big wink which meant that he had sold a Wellfleet to his passenger.

"Seven to go," she thought cheerfully as she heard the senator, red-faced after his oratory, telling everybody what a wonderful machine the Wellfleet was.

The score went down to six that same afternoon, when the Rivals' nearest neighbor bought a motor wagon, and to five the next day, when Papa persuaded Doc Dougall, the druggist, that he needed a Wellfleet to deliver prescriptions in a hurry.

"He hardly ever has to deliver any," Papa confided to Crissy, "but he needed a good excuse for his wife. She says that horseless carriages are—"

"Noisy, smelly things," put in Crissy, who by now knew all the arguments both for and against automobiles. "She'll change her mind. But who are we going to sell the rest to?"

"The birds in the treetops, for all I know," said Papa. "That man over in Harding that I was counting on so strong bought an Oldsmobile runabout after I wore myself out talking up the Wellfleet. The truth is, there's lots of competition, with everybody and his brother building horseless carriages and more people starting in business all the time."

The day before Papa's birthday, a carriage dealer from Oakdale sent in an order for a Wellfleet for one of his customers.

"That was an unexpected one," said Papa. "We need more of the same."

Crissy thought that four more unexpected sales weren't very likely to happen, and she spent one whole afternoon writing down the names of everybody she knew and then crossing them off again either because Papa had already tried them or because Crissy knew they would never buy an automobile anyway. The Bingham Motor Company, she thought dismally, might turn out to be only a lovely dream, after all.

"Some people just aren't the type to buy automobiles," she told Papa, "and some don't have the money, and some—"

"Don't be telling me," said Papa. "Let's think about something pleasant. How about my birthday? What are you going to do about that?"

"Don't you wish you knew?" cried Crissy, forgetting all her worries for a minute. "It's a wonderful, wonderful surprise!"

She had a good deal of trouble keeping Papa quiet through breakfast the next day, because he kept demanding his birthday surprise, even though he already had a necktie, which Aunt Henrietta had knitted for him out of dark green silk, and a handkerchief which Susan-Cat, looking indignant, presented to him in a package tied around her neck.

"All right!" Crissy glanced out of the window and saw Jed driving up in a Wellfleet, which he promptly abandoned, with its motor still running. "The surprise is outside!" She led Papa to the Wellfleet. "Please get in. No, not on the driver's side. That's for me."

While Aunt Henrietta stood on the porch looking alarmed and Papa sat beside Crissy looking astonished,

Crissy started down the street, muttering instructions to herself and neatly rounding the corner by Hawkins'.

"I'm amazed!" said Papa as she headed out by the park and cautiously threaded her way past a boy on a bicycle and a man with a horse and wagon.

"I'm astounded!" said Papa as she bravely crossed River Street and drew up in front of the Carriage Works.

"I'm stupefied!" he said as she started up again and headed straight down River Street.

"I'm— Hey!" he said as she turned her head to look at a white poodle dog with pompons on its legs, a tassel on its tail, and a ruff around its neck. "Hey!"

He grabbed the tiller, but not before Crissy had driven straight into the scalloped hedge which surrounded Banker Cassoway's huge brick house.

"And now," said Papa, "I *am* amazed. Also flabbergasted. *And* dumfounded!"

Crissy uncovered her eyes and looked cautiously around. The nose of the Wellfleet was all the way through the hedge, and Crissy and Papa were staring over the top. On the other side, Banker Cassoway peered at them from behind a snowball bush, where he had leaped to safety from his favorite garden bench.

"Excuse m-me," Crissy stammered, trying to think what Aunt Henrietta would say after demolishing a hedge. "It— it's a lovely m-morning."

Banker Cassoway looked at her anxious face, and Crissy
looked back, thinking how much his expression reminded

her of the "stern and rock-bound coast" in the poem. To
her astonishment, a crack suddenly appeared in the rocks,
and Banker Cassoway began to laugh, rather creakily as
though he was not accustomed to it but still as though he
was enjoying himself.

"Yes, it is," he agreed. "An especially lovely morning. Now how are you going to get out of there?"

"I—I don't know," said Crissy, brushing a branch out of her face. "I didn't learn how to back up yet."

"Change places with me," said Papa. "I'll back it out."

"No rush," said Mr. Cassoway. "I don't have this much excitement with my morning walk every day."

Crissy looked at Papa. She wanted to say that if Mr. Cassoway bought a Wellfleet he could run it into his hedge for excitement any time he wanted to, but she was afraid Mr. Cassoway, who now looked like a rock-bound coast again, would think she was impertinent. Papa backed the Wellfleet out of the hedge, with a great rending of twigs and showering of leaves.

"Loan me a rake and I'll clean it all up," Crissy offered.

"Rake's in the carriage house back there."

Mr. Cassoway gestured toward the barn, which was almost as handsome as the house, only smaller. Crissy started off at a trot. This was a fine way to celebrate Papa's birthday, she told herself crossly, and all because of a poodle that had just had a fancy haircut!

"The place has to look nice for Sarah Belle's wedding reception," said Mr. Cassoway, "or I wouldn't bother."

Crissy immediately felt worse about the hedge. Sarah Belle Cassoway's wedding was going to be next week, one of the social events of the summer, even though everybody wondered how Mrs. Cassoway was going to get her husband out of the house long enough to attend the ceremony.

"The bank to the house, the house to the bank," she complained repeatedly to Aunt Henrietta. "That's where he goes, and nowhere else."

"Let the ladies go to parties and such," Mr. Cassoway always retorted. "I can afford to do what I please, and staying home is it."

"Fancy dresses!" Mr. Cassoway muttered to Papa. "Flowers! Palms! String quartet! Wedding presents! And—" He gazed at Papa with a look of astonishment. "Just the thing! That's what I'll do. You send me one of those things." He gestured toward the Wellfleet. "Sarah Belle's just crazy enough to like it, and so's that young what's-his-name she's going to marry. First thing in the morning, now."

He turned on his heel and strode toward the house with the relieved air of a man who has settled a worrisome problem. Crissy finished raking up the scattered leaves and twigs, added them to a pile of rubbish back of the carriage house, and returned the rake. Papa grinned at her.

"You want to drive?" he asked.

"Certainly I want to drive," said Crissy. "Papa, now we don't have to sell but three more!"

Crissy drove shakily home, resolving to look neither to left nor to right.

"Even though a dragon walked by, with a pink bow on

his tail," she declared. "Papa, Peg never ran into a hedge in all her life, did she?"

"Never." Papa chuckled. "Don't tell her about the Wellfleet, though, or she'll probably try."

Aunt Henrietta rushed to the door as they drove up.

"How did you get along?" she demanded. "It's dangerous, of course, but Chauncey says lots of ladies are driving now." She looked from Papa to Crissy. "Well, tell me about it!"

Papa winked at Crissy.

"It was a great surprise," he said solemnly. "A great surprise for everybody."

9

JUBILEE

"Issycray!" shouted Elmo from the open kitchen door. "Istenlay! E'reway ichray!"

Crissy did wish that Elmo would give up pig Latin, especially when he had something interesting to say, because it took too long to translate it. She fumbled her way through his announcement and didn't believe a word of it.

"Who's rich?" she asked coldly.

"We are!" cried Elmo, returning to English in his excitement. "Papa and Mama and the baby and me. A whole thousand dollars' worth."

"Oh, you are not!"

Crissy thought that on as hot a day as this Elmo ought to be thinking about wading in the Branch instead of making up tall stories about being rich.

"We are!" Elmo insisted. "Papa's Cousin Randolph out West died and left us a thousand dollars!" He gathered speed as he went on with his story. "And do you know what we're going to do? We're going to buy a Wellfleet. Papa's coming down to see your papa about it this afternoon."

This time Crissy did believe him.

"Two more to go!" she counted in her mind. "But only a week to do it in. Oh, dear!"

"Well?" asked Elmo. "Can't you say anything?"

"I was struck dumb," said Crissy, not staying that way very long. "I certainly think you're lucky. Are you going to get to drive it?"

"Yes siree, I am! Just as soon as Papa learns. And so's Mama, too, and the baby whenever she's old enough. So don't be thinking you're the only pebble on the beach."

As she watched Elmo jump the fence into his own back yard, Crissy thought that being a pebble on a beach would be rather restful nowadays. Aunt Henrietta was worrying around with all the last-minute things that the Diamond

Jubilee Committee had to attend to, and Crissy was her official errand girl. Right this minute, in fact, Crissy was supposed to be on her way to pick up the programs down at the *Gazette* and also the printed ribbon badges which out-of-town visitors would wear during the celebration. Almost the only good feature of the errand-running, she thought, was that Aunt Henrietta let her drive Peg practically any time she wanted to.

"She probably thinks Peg is nothing at all to drive after the Wellfleet," thought Crissy. "It's lucky she doesn't know about that hedge."

The hedge had apparently healed fast, because the *Gazette* had had an elaborate account of the wedding and reception, further described by Aunt Henrietta, who had attended, and nobody had said a word about a hedge with a hole in it. The new Wellfleet, gift of the bride's father, had been mentioned, however, both in the *Gazette* and by several guests.

"First time anybody ever gave an automobile for a wedding present in this town, I guess," Crissy told Peg as they started off after the programs.

She was glad that animals didn't understand everything people said, because hearing so much about automobiles lately would certainly have hurt Peg's feelings.

"And I wouldn't exactly blame her," thought Crissy, re-

membering that Papa said that sometime there might not
be any horses at all on the streets.

"They'll all live on farms," Papa had said in one of his
descriptions of what he always called the motor age, which,
he declared firmly, was practically at hand.

Crissy hoped that the day when horses would live only
on farms would not come right away, because she felt sure
that Peg, who had always lived in town, would be dread-
fully lonesome in the country.

"You'll never have to be away from us," Crissy promised
Peg, who twitched an ear as though she understood perfectly. "After all, an automobile is only a machine, but
you're practically a person!"

The days went on, with more and more to do in each
one, because everybody who ran into difficulties also ran
to Aunt Henrietta to get them straightened out. Costumes
for the pageant, plans for the parade and for the decorated
floats that would go in it, the big picnic out at Sadler's
Grove, the fireworks display at night—all called for attention from Aunt Henrietta, assisted by Crissy.

"It's awful to be efficient, Hen," Papa told her. "Gets you
into lots of trouble."

"As soon as the Jubilee's over, I'm going to give up
efficiency," Aunt Henrietta vowed. "I'll just put on my
new hat and act helpless."

Crissy couldn't imagine Aunt Henrietta acting very help-

less, except when, now and then, she did put on her beautiful new hat and her pink linen dress and treated Dr. Agnew
as though he knew everything and she knew nothing at all.

"Hen's a smart woman," Papa told Crissy, "only she
didn't have sense enough to act as though she wasn't until
now. Shows what a second look at a man will do."

Crissy decided that grownups were even more peculiar
than she had realized, but she could see plainly enough that
Dr. Agnew liked the new Aunt Henrietta, who hung on
his arm and smiled, much better than he had the Aunt
Henrietta who had devoted her time to seeing that everything was running like clockwork.

As each day passed, Crissy worried harder about Papa's
automobiles. Even Papa, although he pretended that there
was nothing to worry about, began to look upset and irri-
table.

"Papa," said Crissy timidly one day, "couldn't we get
somebody else's automobiles to sell if we don't sell our
twenty for Mr. Wellfleet?"

Papa shook his head.

"We probably could, but I promised Mr. Wellfleet that
if we failed at this I'd come back and sell carriages for him
again. And a promise is a promise."

Crissy had forgotten the promise, but she agreed with
Papa that it had to be kept. It gave her a very cheerful
feeling, though, to have Papa say "we" as though she had

really been of some help to him with the automobiles. Even on the day before the Jubilee, when she went down to the Works to help decorate the float which Mr. Wellfleet was putting in the parade, she had not quite given up hope of seeing the Bingham Motor Company doing business in Granite City.

" 'In the shadow of a great affliction,' " said Jed Haley, who was entangled in yards of white crepe paper, with which he was constructing an elaborate swan which would ride in the parade on a company farm wagon. "(John Greenleaf Whittier, born 1807, died 1892.) Crepe paper! And me a workingman! Here, hold this end, if you will. It rolls up every time I let go. Did you hear that I am about to go on the stage again?"

Crissy shook her head and hoped that the paper swan was going to look less like a duck before the day was over.

"I have been signed up for the summer Chautauqua circuit, starting next week," said Jed. "Accompanied by the marionettes, of course. More evenings with Shakespeare. Mr. Wellfleet is giving me time off to fulfill my engagements."

"Why, how wonderful!" Crissy could still remember a program she had seen in the Chautauqua tent last summer, with a magician who made a girl disappear into thin air. "I mean, it is if you—"

"If I get paid," said Jed, "which I do, and very gener-

ously. So generously, in fact, that I shall find it necessary
to buy a motor vehicle with which to transport myself and
marionettes to our various destinations, all of which are in
Michigan so far. Kindly tell your father that a prospect is
waiting to work out a special design—one seat for me and
an enclosed space in the back for the marionettes and their
small portable stage. I understand that the larger companies call this a custom-built vehicle."

"Oh, Jed!" Crissy almost hugged him, cigar and all.
"Thank you very, very much, even if it is too late."

"Not too late yet," said Jed stoutly. "How many more
do you need?"

"One now," said Crissy dejectedly, "and there's just
today left."

"And all day tomorrow, I should suppose," said Jed.
"The Jubilee won't actually be over until the last visitor
goes home tomorrow night. I'd tell Mr. Wellfleet that, if
he's of a mind to be technical about it.

"He probably is," said Crissy. "He doesn't want Papa
to sell automobiles. He said it was a double-dyed mistake."

"That's what I heard," said Jed, "some time ago. Now
then, can you assist me with a little advice about the curve
of this creature's neck?"

The swan turned out to be a work of art, and Crissy
added two pink water lilies to the sea of blue crepe paper
on which the swan was anchored. She gathered up the

pieces of leftover paper to decorate the Wellfleet which Papa would drive in the parade. She also intended to tie red-white-and-blue bows on her braids and around Susan-Cat's neck in honor of the occasion.

Nothing seemed as exciting as Crissy had expected, now that it looked as though maybe there might not be any Bingham Motor Company and Papa might not be an automobile salesman any more. Crissy didn't even care much whether she rode in the parade in the Wellfleet or not. It would have been just as much fun to drive Peg, she thought, but Papa had promised Peg to Elmo for the day, since the Hawkins' new Wellfleet was not quite ready to go out of the paint shop yet.

Crissy had not seen Papa all day, but she knew that he was rushing around talking to all the people who had shown the slightest interest in automobiles and urging them to place an order. Crissy was waiting on the front steps when he came home for supper.

"Did anybody buy one?" she asked before he was even up the steps.

Papa shook his head.

"They all have more excuses than I could think up in six months." He looked at Crissy's woebegone face. "There's one chance that I know of, though. If Jethro Blade—"

"My fat friend?" asked Crissy. "That I sold the automobile to at the race?"

"The same one," said Papa. "If he gets back from his trip out West to buy cattle, he just might want a motor wagon. He was talking some about one before he left. He wasn't back today, but he might be tomorrow, and if he is he'll surely come to the Jubilee."

Papa sounded so extremely cheerful that Crissy suspected he was only pretending to feel that way.

"Lots of people from away will be coming to the Jubilee," said Crissy. "I should think one of them would surely want a Wellfleet."

"Don't think I won't be trying," Papa assured her, "but just remember that we've done our best and so we mustn't have any regrets, no matter how it comes out."

When Crissy kissed Papa good night and trotted off to bed, she was very uncertain about whether to feel sad or hopeful.

"I don't see how I can bear another whole day of not knowing for sure," she told Susan-Cat.

Even before she had finished eating her breakfast the next morning, Elmo was knocking on the back door.

"Let's go see the Chinese fireworks," he said.

Crissy looked questioningly at Papa and Aunt Henrietta. Maybe she shouldn't go, with things so uncertain about Papa's automobiles, but Papa nodded at her and said, "Go along! You can't miss that." Aunt Henrietta didn't say anything, because she was busy getting ready to go to the parade with Dr. Agnew, who was coming for her as soon as he had made his morning calls.

Just as Crissy and Elmo were starting off, Mr. Wellfleet reined up his handsome team of grays and handed Crissy an envelope.

"Give it to your papa, please," he said. "I'm too busy to stop right now."

Crissy rushed inside and gave Papa the envelope, which looked exactly like the ones Mr. Wellfleet always used when he sent Papa a list of carriage dealers that he wanted called on right away. Mr. Wellfleet certainly wasn't wasting any time getting Papa started on carriages again, Crissy thought crossly.

"Crissy!" Elmo yelled from the sidewalk. "Come on! We'll miss the whole thing!"

In spite of feeling so much in suspense about the Bingham Motor Company, Crissy couldn't help a tingle of excitement as she and Elmo neared River Street and listened for the Chinese firecrackers.

"They're starting already!" said Elmo. "Can't you go any faster?"

She and Elmo tore around the corner and saw the wire which Granite City's two rival Chinese laundrymen had rigged across River Street for their firecrackers.

Just as in other years as far back as Crissy could remember, the two were standing solemnly in their shop doorways, one on each side of River Street, and listening to the popping of the firecrackers which they had ordered from China for this one day of the year.

Crissy always liked to walk along this block on River Street, first on one side of the street and then on the other, to stare at the mysterious Chinese characters on the two shop windows and to sniff the odd odor of steam, incense, and Chinese cooking which floated through the dark doorways. Papa always insisted that the writing on one window said "Hurrah for the U.S.A." and that the window opposite said "The Stars and Stripes Forever." Crissy knew that was a joke, but since she didn't know the laundrymen's names, she called one "Hurrah" and the other "Stars-and-Stripes."

"In my mind, I mean," she told Elmo. "I wouldn't dream of calling them that out loud."

Everybody else in town called them Cholly, both of them, but Crissy thought that was very impolite, too. She nodded shyly to Hurrah in his doorway and then walked across to nod to Stars-and-Stripes, too. Stars-and-Stripes bowed back politely and handed Crissy a long string of red firecrackers, gay with gold Chinese writing.

"You want to thlow?" he asked, gesturing to the long wire.

"Oh, yes, thank you!"

Stars-and-Stripes lit the first firecracker with a burning piece of punk, and Crissy quickly threw the whole string over the wire just as she had seen the two Chinese do so many times.

Bang! Pop! Bang! went the firecrackers one after another.

"Chinese firecrackers don't have the same expression as American ones," Crissy whispered to Elmo. "They sound sort of foreign."

Elmo nodded. Crissy thanked Stars-and-Stripes for letting her shoot off the firecrackers and walked back to Hurrah's side of the street. Hurrah bowed, handed her a string of his firecrackers to throw over the wire, and gravely received her thanks. For a long time Crissy and Elmo watched as the two Chinese took turns with their firecrackers. Everybody knew that there was intense rivalry between the two about their fireworks, but nobody would have suspected it from the polite bows which they exchanged as each string of firecrackers sputtered to an end. It seemed no time at all until the big clock on the courthouse boomed out ten strokes.

"Oh, my goodness!" Crissy tugged at Elmo's sleeve. "The parade's in an hour, and I have to help decorate Papa's Wellfleet."

The children scurried through the streets, past lawns studded with tiny American flags. Sleek horses hitched to decorated carriages stood in the driveways, and excited children chased each other across the wide porches.

At home, Crissy could smell the big ham which Aunt Henrietta had put in the oven to bake for the picnic. Peering into the barn, Crissy saw that Papa and Peg were gone and that the Wellfleet, polished and shining, was waiting to be decorated.

"Papa's gone to hunt for Jethro Blade probably," Crissy decided hopefully.

Assisted by Susan-Cat, who ran after every streamer like a kitten, Crissy wound crepe paper around the spokes of the wheels and in and out of the steering wheel which Mr. Wellfleet had finally adopted as being more up-to-date than the tiller. It had been more fun helping Jed decorate the farm wagon, Crissy thought, but of course there was no room on Papa's Wellfleet for anything as complicated as a swan.

Dr. Agnew, in his best gray suit with a heavy gold watch chain festooned across his vest, drove up in a great hurry and took Aunt Henrietta away with him. Aunt Henrietta looked lovely, Crissy thought wistfully, wishing for once in her life that she had golden hair like Martha May and a hat with roses on it like Aunt Henrietta.

"I'll finish that," said Papa, arriving on foot at the barn door, "and you can get ready to go. I took Peg and the carriage around for the Hawkins."

"Did Mr. Blade come back?"

Papa shook his head.

"It's pretty early in the day yet. He'll likely show up later."

Crissy rushed upstairs to rebraid her hair and to tie a red-white-and-blue bow on the end of each braid. With her blue sash and her white dress, which was only a little mussed from her trip down to see the Chinese firecrackers, she decided that she looked as well as could be expected.

She wasted several precious minutes finding Susan-Cat, who was asleep in the coal bin, and persuading her to hold still while Crissy tied a red-white-and-blue bow around her unwilling neck. Susan seemed not a bit interested in being dressed up, but she looked very handsome in spite of herself after Crissy had sprinkled her all over with Aunt Henrietta's talcum powder to cover up the coal dust.

"Here we go," said Papa, whistling a cheerful tune just as though he had forgotten all about the Bingham Motor Company. "Susan, you sit in the middle."

"If Papa can be cheerful, I can, too," Crissy decided, whistling the chorus along with him.

It was hard to be sad, anyway, with all the excitement down at the corner where the parade was going to start. As they hurried down the side street, with Crissy craning her neck for a glimpse of Jethro Blade, she could see the Granite City Brass Band ready to start off in their red-and-blue uniforms. The marshal of the day and his aides were skirmishing up and down the line of march on nervous

saddle horses. Crissy saw Elmo and his family with Peg
in the carriage division. The carriage was hung with bunt-
ing, and Elmo was sitting proudly in the driver's seat.

"We belong farther down the line," said Papa. "The
automobile section certainly won't be big. In fact, maybe
we'll be all there is of it."

Crissy was happy to see that the Rivals, taking great care
not to notice each other, had driven in with their Wellfleets
lavishly decorated with huge bouquets of flowers. The Han-
overs, very gay with a party of visitors from Detroit, dashed
up in their Panhard and found a place at the head of the
automobile division. Dr. Agnew and Aunt Henrietta arrived in a few minutes, and Elmo came running back to
report that Captain Dowling was driving his Wellfleet
motor wagon up with the rest of the fire department.
Presently a little Oldsmobile runabout and a big steamer
from Oakdale appeared to bring up the rear. Crissy was
glad that she and Papa were as far as possible from the
visiting steamer, because in her search for sales points for
the gasoline-powered Wellfleet she had read that steamers
sometimes blew up if everything did not work exactly right.

"They may blow up now and then," said Papa, "but
they go like the wind the rest of the time, just like a steam
locomotive."

"Mr. Blade might drive his other machine in the parade,"
Crissy suggested.

"If he's back," said Papa. "Well, it's a good display of automobiles, anyway. Next Fourth of July there'll be four times as many, for as sure as I'm sitting here, the day's coming when— There's the band. Let's go."

He slid out of the driver's seat, shoved Crissy over behind the wheel, and settled Susan-Cat comfortably between them.

"I guess it's safe," he told Crissy with a twinkle. "I don't see any hedges around here."

"Oh, Papa!" Crissy was almost speechless with bliss. "Are you sure it's all right? Absolutely, positively sure?"

She had dreamed ever since last winter of driving the Wellfleet in the parade, but she had felt, after the hedge, that it was a dream that would never come true.

"And now it has," thought Crissy, wondering if any more dreams were going to come true today.

She glanced quickly over the crowd in search of Jethro Blade, Papa's great hope, and the Wellfleet swerved a little out of line.

"You drive. I'll look," Papa warned. "Remember the hedge."

The rest of the day was a jumbled blur for Crissy, with all sorts of pleasant things mixed in with her worries about the Bingham Motor Company. The presentation of prizes at the reviewing stand, where Crissy, with Susan-Cat tucked under her arm, received a blue ribbon from the mayor for being the youngest automobile driver in the parade. The picnic at Sadler's Grove, where Crissy for once ate all the potato salad she wanted. The historical pageant at the outdoor amphitheater, where Elmo and Crissy exchanged cheerful glances when Martha May forgot her lines and had to be prompted. The little supper party at home, where Aunt Henrietta, blushing and pretty, announced that she and Dr. Agnew would be married in the fall.

"But no Jethro Blade," Crissy fretted. "And no Papa, either."

Papa, she supposed, was trying to sell automobiles, and Jethro Blade might be anywhere between Granite City and the western plains.

"Only I hope he's here," Crissy wished desperately.

Papa finally appeared, looking tired and dusty, just when it was dark enough so that the fireflies were making flickering lights across the lawn.

"Let's go down and see the fireworks," he suggested. "They'll be extra-fancy this year."

"Papa," said Crissy, "did Jethro—"

"Didn't get back," said Papa, "or if he did I didn't see him." Papa bustled around lighting the oil lamps on the Wellfleet. "Let's get going, shall we? We don't want to miss anything."

Crissy knew that Papa was hurrying her along because he didn't want her to fuss about losing the Bingham Motor

Company. He speeded up the motor so that conversation was impossible, and they roared off downtown.

"Here's a good place to see." Papa guided the machine close to the sidewalk on River Street, with its rows of dark stores. "We can sit right in the Wellfleet and get a good look at everything."

As usual, the fireworks would be set off from the top of the River Street bridge, with boards laid across the top of the bridge and a ladder down to the street for the hasty descent of the man who ran the display.

Fireworks or no fireworks, Crissy was glad that it was dark, because she was afraid that she might be going to cry just the least little bit by way of mourning for the Bingham Motor Company. A big tear was starting to roll down her cheek when the first of the skyrockets went off from the top of the bridge. Papa touched her arm just as the light from a whole row of pinwheels lit up the street for a minute.

"Look that way!" he said gently.

Crissy looked and saw golden letters illuminated on the store window beside her. "Bingham Motor Company," she thought it said.

"But it can't," she cried.

Suddenly all the lights went on in the store, and Crissy was staring speechless at a window that did say "Bingham Motor Company—Automobiles and Motor Wagons" in curly gold letters. Jed and Mr. Wellfleet rushed out to greet her.

"Thought you were never going to look," Jed grumbled.

Crissy stared in delight at the spacious showroom, with a shining Wellfleet sitting in splendor in each of the two wide windows. Everybody seemed to be talking at once.

"Papa," said Crissy, "it just can't be!"

"Oh, yes, it can," said Papa. "You know that note Mr. Wellfleet left? It was an order for a machine for himself and an offer to rent me this store. So Jed and I got busy right away, and—"

"The twentieth automobile!" said Crissy. "But Mr. Wellfleet said—"

"Never mind what I said!" roared Mr. Wellfleet. "A man can change his mind, can't he? Can't shut down the automobile shop and have people say I failed at it, can I? It's going to be the Wellfleet Carriage and Automobile Works from now on, and what do you think of that?"

"I think it's wonderful!" cried Crissy.

Mr. Wellfleet looked pleased, but his words were as gruff as ever.

"May be wonderful and may not," he stated. "A man has to keep up with the times, but it's going to be quite a chore. Going to have to run all over the country and find out how the other automobile manufacturers operate. Going to have to get special steel bodies and new designs and everything different if I'm going to get my share of the business, and—"

Crissy left Mr. Wellfleet counting his sorrows and stepped back outside to admire the Bingham Motor Company and the fireworks both at once. The huge set piece of Niagara Falls which would end the Jubilee in a blaze of glory spilled its fire on the top of the bridge, and Crissy stood imagining that already she could hear the sound of horses trotting down the streets and disappearing forever and the rush of automobiles hurrying faster and faster to take their places.

"Jed!" she called suddenly. "Jed! I'm a poet! Listen!

'The Jubilee is over with the setting of the sun,
But the Bingham Motor Company is only just begun.'

(Crissy Bingham, born 1891—)"

Jed removed his hat, bowed ceremoniously, and neatly finished off the verse:

"And with Susan-Cat a-purring, we all do surely feel
That business will be rushing, with our Crissy at the
    wheel."